COURTLANDT CANBY

| a history of flight

*This book was designed and
produced by Erik Nitsche
International, S.A., Geneva.
It was printed and bound in
Switzerland by Heliogravure
Centrale, Lausanne.
The engravings were made by
Heliogravure Centrale,
Lausanne. The text paper is
white gravure 140 gr/m². This
book is published simultane-
ously in Canada by
McClelland & Stewart Ltd.,
25 Hollinger Road, Toronto 16.
The Library of Congress has
cataloged this volume of
The New Illustrated Library
of Science and Invention
under card number 63-8111.
Suggested Decimal Classification
for this series is 500.*

First edition - April, 1963

a history of flight

THE NEW ILLUSTRATED LIBRARY OF SCIENCE AND INVENTION

Designed and produced
by Erik Nitsche

Hawthorn Books Inc.
Publishers, New York

contents

"The airplane is of course only a machine," Antoine de Saint-Exupéry once wrote, "but what an instrument of analysis ! This instrument has shown us the real face of earth. . . . Up here, observing man from our portholes, we find ourselves judging him on a cosmic scale. . . . We find ourselves rereading our own history."

Saint-Exupéry's evocations of man-in-flight were written some time ago. Today the earth, viewed from the windows of a jetliner, seems much smaller than it did to Saint-Exupéry, while the universe above has grown large and challenging. At 40,000 feet the sun, pouring down its clean, glittering light, is no longer just a hot button pasted at the edge of our familiar sky, but has taken on the appearance of the distant, incandescent star it really is. Miles below, one can glimpse, between breaks in the cottony cloud-cover, the tiny works of man—the gashes in the earth, the speckled cities bunched at the hubs of rivers and highways. Of man himself, nothing can be seen.

The earth looks even smaller, the universe even larger from a research plane flying at the edge of space, or from a Tiros satellite orbiting the globe. Human flight, in a very real sense, has shrunk the oceans to swimming pools, the continents to pastures, the earth itself to a minor planet of a minor star. The achievement of human flight, by drawing more closely together the peoples and the nations of the earth, has begun to create throughout the world a new realization of a common destiny. Blending insensibly in recent years into the exploration of space, it has enlarged our thinking, too, by opening up the nearby reaches of the solar system for our inspection.

The history of man is thousands of years old, but the history of the airplane is hardly a century old. In this brief period we have progressed from the Wrights' first hop, only a few feet off the ground, to the flight of the X-15 to the top of the atmosphere at 4,000 miles per hour. Only during the last few years of this brief history has aviation become a major power in the world. It first showed its might in World War II. Designers and scientists since then have been probing the frontiers of aerodynamic knowledge as never before, while the passenger plane has become the dominant form of the world's transportation. Between 1948 and 1958 the major airlines of the United States, in terms of revenue, elbowed out the major railroads for top position, and began to carry more people across the Atlantic than the steamship lines. Yet in this age of swift jet transports and supersonic bombers, many of the pioneers of the earliest years of aviation are still alive. Orville Wright himself survived the Second World War.

Never has there been such a history—so much in so short a time. No wonder the chroniclers of man's past have only just begun to record the history of aviation. It has been too close to us, it is too new, it all happened too fast.

Less known and remembered, because much older than the history of the airplane, is another history—that of man's first conquest of the air in balloons. No pioneers survive from that period; only the quaintly charming colored prints in museums and old books which give us the impression that balloon ascensions must have been prime sport, but surely were of no great importance. Yet one of these old prints may give us pause. It shows the earth as seen from a balloon in 1786, many thousands of feet up, with the landscape far below glimpsed through breaks in the cottony cloud-cover. This is a view we thought belonged to the age of the modern airliner. Other old prints begin to tell their story : enormous crowds in Paris watching with awe and overflowing excitement the first ascension of two men in a hydrogen balloon ; brave pioneers writhing to death in their flaming balloons or plunging helplessly to the earth below ; the incredible courage of Jacques Garnerin, who dared to make the first parachute jump over Paris from a great height ; the triumph of Henri Giffard, as his crude, powered dirigible of 1852 responded, though feebly, to his efforts to control its flight.

The first men left the earth in a balloon in 1783. For three years thereafter the public excitement was at fever pitch. Its fervor can only be compared to the wave of emotion that swept the world after Lindbergh crossed the Atlantic alone in 1927. And rightly so ; for those long-dead people had caught a glimpse of the wonder of flight—the liberation from the earth, the exploration of a new world, the courage of the airmen who were willing to risk their lives, partly for sport, but mostly to enlarge the horizons of mankind. The orbiting astronauts of our day share the same spirit. "I am eagle, I am eagle" exulted Russia's second astronaut, Gherman Titov, as he flew through space. The American, Malcolm S. Carpenter, was impressed, like all the astronauts, with the sunsets and sunrises he encountered. "Boy," he said, "they are more beautiful than anything I have ever seen on earth." Flight has achieved a new dimension, but little has really changed.

1 "... we will spring into the air with the impetuousness of the eagle."

Jean-Jacques Rousseau believed in the possibility of flight. "At first we will only skim the surface of the earth like young starlings," he wrote with typical enthusiasm, "but soon, emboldened by practice and experience, we will spring into the air with the impetuousness of the eagle, diverting ourselves by watching the childish behaviour of the little men crawling miserably around on the earth below us." Rousseau, of course, had no idea how man was going to fly —except that he was going to fly like the birds. This idea had haunted mankind from earliest times. And from the dawn of history man's attempts to emulate the skill of the birds had been marked by the pathetic, broken bodies of adventurers who had tried to flap their way through the air and had crashed, Icarus-like, amidst the wreckage of their artificial wings.

Heavier-than-air flight would not be possible until the early 1900's, when the technical means had been developed that would bring it within man's grasp. But there were other ways of getting into the air. Man's first flight, his first incredible escape from the confines of the earth, took place in France well over a century before the Wright brothers lifted their crude machine from the sands of Kitty Hawk. The first great age of flight opened in Avignon, in November 1782. Joseph Montgolfier, a paper manufacturer with an inventive turn of mind, sat musing by the fire. Noting the smoke and hot air rushing upwards, he was seized with an inspiration. Asking his landlady for rags of silk, he constructed a simple cloth balloon on the spot, filled it with hot air, and watched with satisfaction as it fluttered quickly to the ceiling. The lighter-than-air balloon had been invented.

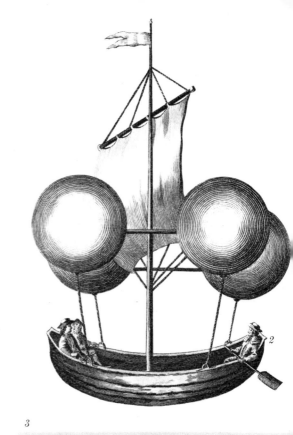

By the spring of 1783 Joseph Montgolfier, with his brother Etienne, had put together the world's first balloon, a huge sphere of paper-lined linen. On June 4, filled with hot air from a fire of wool and straw, it rose up some 6,000 feet before a large crowd at Annonay, the brothers' home town. Surprisingly, the importance of the event was immediately recognized. At the insistence of the Academy of the Sciences at Paris the brothers constructed a new balloon, which was launched at Versailles in September in the presence of the royal pair. A sheep, a duck, and a cock were carried aloft on a free flight of some two miles. Like the astronautic chimpanzees of a later day, they managed to survive the ordeal. The sheep was rewarded with a berth in the Royal Menagerie. In the meantime the physicist, Jacques Charles, with the Robert brothers, mechanics, had harnessed the lifting power of a recently discovered gas called "inflammable air"—known today as hydrogen. Their first balloon had flown for 15 miles on August 27, only to be attacked and destroyed by terrified peasants on its landing.

With public excitement mounting, the stage was set for human flight. An enthusiastic young scientist, Pilâtre de Rozier, volunteered to make the attempt in the Versailles balloon, rebuilt with a gallery around its base. After some preliminary, tethered flights in October, the great balloon, belching smoke and flame, sailed up at last in free flight on November 21 from the gardens of La Muette outside Paris, carrying de Rozier and the Marquis d'Arlandes. As they arose, d'Arlandes repeatedly waved his handkerchief to reassure the crowd below. Pilâtre, busy with the balloon, shouted, "You aren't

2 Ingenious balloon machine of Jesuit
Francesco Lana, proposed in 1670, used
thin copper globes with air removed to
raise ship. Although unworkable, the plan
was much admired and discussed
by Lana's contemporaries.
3 Japanese kite attests to the skill very
early acquired by the Chinese and other
Orientals in using air currents for flight.
4 Jean-Pierre Blanchard's beating wing
flying machine was tested between 1781 and
1783, hung from a rope with a
counterweight. After invention of the
balloon in 1783, Blanchard attached lower
half of the machine to his balloon
in attempt to steer it.

4

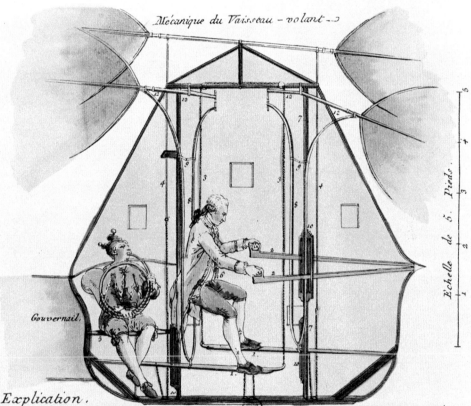

Mécanique du Vaisseau - volant

Echelle de 5. Pieds.

Gouvernail.

Explication.

1. Pédales en forme de levier du second genre.
2. Bascules en forme de levier du second genre.
3. Gardes de Correspondance qui soulevent les Pédales alternativement.
4. Cordes qui servent au mouvement des ailes conductrices et qui font un autre mouvement que celles qui soutiennent.
5. Compagnon de voyage.
6. Pilote aérien.
7. Montants qui soutiennent le Chapiteau.
8. Filets de soutien qui font agir les ailes au moyen des pédales du N.º 1.º
9. Brides mouvantes tant au milieu qu'aux extremités pour empêcher l'écartem.t des Filets du N.º 8
10. Glissoirs qui empêchent l'écartement tant des pédales du N.º 1. que des Bascules N.º 2.
11. Cordes correspondant.s dont les 2. extrémités sont mobiles attachées sous les Pédales du N.º 1.º et passent sous les 2. poulies tenantes au fond de Calle
12. Principales membranes qui servent à adapter les 4. ailes d'ascension.

11

doing anything, and we're hardly moving !"
"Excuse me," answered d'Arlandes, and forked
more straw into the fire. The balloon shot upwards. When its fabric, lit by cinders, started
burning, the two ran around the gallery with
sponges, putting out the fires. And so they flew
for some 25 minutes, skimming the rooftops or
bobbing high as the fire blazed or smoldered.
Avoiding two windmills, they settled down
some five miles from their starting point. Pilâtre
struggled out from beneath the balloon in his
shirt-sleeves, having jettisoned his "redingote"
(which the gathering crowd tore into shreds for
souvenirs). So it fell to the Marquis, still properly
attired, to go and report to the Academy.

The age of flight, however, really began with
the ascension of Charles and the younger Robert
in a hydrogen balloon on December 1. This time
at least half the inhabitants of Paris, perhaps
400,000 persons, witnessed the flight, which
started from the Tuileries gardens. The balloon
itself, moreover, embodied for the first time all
the essential features of later free balloons. As
the great red and yellow globe sailed smoothly
laoft, the aeronauts, with no need to tend a fire,
waved flags and handkerchiefs and shouted
"Vive le Roi !" Overcome by the spectacle, the
immense crowd below "raised their arms to the
heavens with surprise, admiration, joy, and
astonishment. Some wept, fearing for the intrepid scientists, others fell to their knees, overcome by surprise, terror, and an access of tender-
ness. There was not one spectator who did not
identify himself with the aeronauts. . . ."

It was a sparkling winter day. As the aeronauts surveyed the magnificent scene around
them, the mingled shouts and cries of the
immense crowd below came faintly to their
ears. "Oh ! My dear friend," Charles said to
Robert, "how happy we are ! . . . The sky
belongs to us ! What a breathtaking scene !"
This first great flight lasted over two hours, the
balloon landing 27 miles from Paris. Charles
then took it up again alone, after the sun had set,
reaching the dizzy height of nearly 9,000 feet
before he landed. Like the globe-circling astronauts of our time, he saw the sun set twice in
one day. And so human flight had become a
reality. When Benjamin Franklin, who was
supposed to have witnessed one of the first
ascensions, was asked by doubters, "But of what
use is it ?" he answered, "Of what use is a new-
born baby ?"

After these first flights, ballooning became the
craze of Europe. For two years the public could
talk of nothing else. Balloon motifs appeared
on dinner services, coiffures, fans, bookbind-
ings, clocks, and in numerous caricatures. Under
the leadership of Jean-Pierre Blanchard and
Vicenzo Lunardi, ascensions became a favorite
form of public spectacle. In January of 1784
seven people—Pilâtre, Joseph Montgolfier, three
counts, one prince, and a stowaway—went up
together in a huge balloon at Lyon. In June the
first woman passenger, Madame Thible, recited
poetry as she ascended : "Je triomphe, je suis
reine. . . ." Lunardi introduced air travel to
England in September, and was shortly followed into the English air by James Sadler, founder
of a great English aeronautical family.

At the beginning of 1785 Blanchard, with his
American backer Dr. John Jeffries, joined
England and France by air with a perilous flight
across the Channel during which a bottle of

spirits and even the aeronauts' pants had to be jettisoned to keep the ship aloft. The first enthusiasm for ballooning was somewhat dampened by such accidents as the death of brave Pilâtre de Rozier in his own attempt to cross the Channel later that year ; but great showmen like Blanchard, who introduced the art to seven countries, kept it before the public. Exhibition flights were often enhanced by parachute jumps, after the intrepid André-Jacques Garnerin had made the first long jump over Paris in 1797.

By the turn of the century the main lines of free-ballooning had been set, the balloons thereafter merely becoming larger, more decorative ; their flights longer, and the festivals and exhibitions in which they appeared more elaborate. Single names, but more often great families—the Greens, the Sadlers, the Godards —began to dominate lighter-than-air aeronautics. And accidents became more frequent as ballooning spread. After the death of Blanchard in 1809 his wife continued to stage exhibition flights throughout Europe. Ten years later, while setting off fireworks in a night flight, she fell to her death in her flaming balloon, "victim" as her epitaph reads, "of her art and of her intrepidity." Count Zambeccari of Italy suffered an incredible series of accidents in his hybrid hot-air and hydrogen balloon, repeatedly falling into the Adriatic or shooting up so high that his fingers froze, or just managing to escape from his flaming balloon. In 1812, after a final accident, he died of burns.

Garnerin, the parachutist, and Belgian-born Etienne Robertson made many famous flights early in the century. But it was Charles Green of England, with his 504 ascensions between 1821 and 1852, who did as much as anybody to popularize the sport, especially in England. He carried up thousands of persons without an accident. In his famous *Nassau* of red and yellow silk, which stayed in service nearly 40 years, Green made the first long-distance flight, from London into Germany, in 1836—480 miles in 18 hours. A lesser aeronaut of the period, debonair Francisque Arban of France, is remembered for his first balloon-crossing of the Alps in 1849. As a momento of the voyage he threw an empty wine bottle into the high snow fields as he passed over the rugged mountain slopes.

Ballooning was not confined to exhibition flights. Although both Robertson and Gay-Lussac, a young scientist, made rival ascents in 1803 and 1804 to study the upper atmosphere, the most serious scientific flights were those organized by the British Association in mid-century, during which Henry Coxwell and James Glaisher were supposed to have reached the incredible height of about 37,000 feet. Gaston and Albert Tissandier also made high-altitude ascents, one of which, in 1875, caused the death of two people from lack of air. Of scientific interest, too, was the amazing light-weight copper balloon constructed by Jean-François Dupuis-Delcourt, a dedicated inventor and aeronautical historian, in 1844. Lack of funds prevented him from flying it.

A dazzling new period of popular ballooning opened in 1850 when the impresario Arnault of Paris's Hippodrome added balloon ascents by the great aeronaut, Eugène Godard, to his attractions. In no time Godard's flights had become so popular that he found it necessary to

5

impress his whole family—brothers, relatives, and children—into service. The Godard family so dominated French ballooning for half a century thereafter that "Godard" became another word for balloon. The Hippodrome also featured acrobats performing beneath gaily colored balloons, and the "girls of the air," ballerinas dangling amidst cardboard clouds, while a rival establishment, that of the Poitevins, specialized in aerial performances on horseback, or on the backs of bulls (Madame Poitevin often appeared as Europa).

The new balloon craze, which hit London in 1851, brought forth not only the popular rubber balloon for children but also the largest balloons ever constructed. Félix Nadar's *Géant* of 1863 was the first (he was a brilliant artist and ardent aeronaut, who also took the first aerial photograph over Paris in 1858), but it was surpassed the next year by Godard's 18,340 cubic yard *Aigle*. Biggest of all, however, were the giant captive balloons of Henri Giffard, which gave thousands their first exciting taste of aerial flight. Giffard's fourth balloon, installed in Paris in 1878, contained 32,750 cubic yards of hydrogen, stood 165 feet tall, and could raise 50 people at a time in its huge gondola.

In the United States the two leading aeronauts—John C. Wise and Thaddeus C. Lowe—both prepared enormous balloons for transatlantic crossings just before the Civil War, but both were frustrated. Wise tried again in 1873, but his balloon crashed some 40 miles outside of New York. Professor Lowe is far better known for his part in organizing the Balloon Signal Service during the Civil War, whose captive reconnaissance balloons rendered useful service

6

for the Union. As early as 1794 the French "Compagnie d'Aérostiers" had had some success with captive observation balloons, but it was disbanded around 1800. Napoleon, however, was reported to have studied the possibility of invading England by air with a fleet of huge balloons. In 1849 the Austrians launched 100 bomb-carrying balloons over beleagured Venice, but the wind changed and almost all the balloons returned to drop their bombs over the Austrian lines ! A more heroic episode was the successful balloon service organized by the French during the siege of Paris in 1870. Sixty-six balloons—mostly manufactured in railroad stations under trying winter conditions—left the city carrying passengers, letters, and carrier pigeons for flying messages back into Paris again. Some were captured or lost, but most got through.

From the beginning the limitations of the free balloon had been realized. Completely at the mercy of the winds, it was like a sail, drifting with a boat dangling beneath it. No wonder the earliest aeronauts, including Blanchard and Lunardi, vainly attempted to control their ships with a strange variety of oars, rudders, paddle wheels, sails, and even crude propellers. Some seriously proposed the use of captive birds to pull their balloons along. The elongated (and therefore more maneuverable) balloon shape tried by the Robert brothers was a feature, too, in the remarkable dirigible (see cover) projected by General Meusnier in 1785, but never brought to fruition because of his early death. What was needed, everybody knew, was a ship that could swim purposefully through the air like a fish through water. The great George Cayley, father of the airplane, turned to the dirigible after 1816, envisaging many of its basic principles as well as steam propulsion and a type of rigid dirigible.

Mechanical propulsion was first applied to the airship by two Frenchmen associated with the famous Hippodrome. Pierre Jullien, humbly born clockmaker of genius, after flying two model, clockwork-powered dirigibles at the Hippodrome, built (but never flew) his fish-shaped, full-scale *Précurseur* in 1852. Equipped with rudders and elevators at the stern, its design was aerodynamically sound. His ship was indeed a precursor in every sense, for in that same year Henri Giffard, later famous for his captive balloons, took off from the Hippodrome in the first successful motor-driven flight in history. An inventor to be ranked with the Wrights and Montgolfiers, Giffard owed much to Jullien. His cigar-like dirigible, 132 feet long, was driven by a three horsepower steam engine and propeller, slung below its belly, and would make six miles per hour. It could not steer directly into the wind, but it was decidedly controllable. Describing that first brief trip from Paris to Trappes, Giffard wrote, "I could definitely feel the action of the rudder, for as soon as I lightly pulled one of the two maneuvering ropes I immediately saw the horizon turning around me." An eyewitness later recalled "the enthusiasm of the public and our strange sensation when we saw the intrepid inventor rising upwards in his apparatus, with the harsh sound of escaping steam taking the place of the usual flag salute to the public."

Although the papers called Giffard, after his flight, "the Fulton of aerial navigation," he was

8 *Almanac of 1784 features pioneer balloons of period, including (at center) original Charles-Robert hydrogen balloon, rebuilt and elongated in attempt to improve control.*

9 *Aerial voyage by Blanchard and l'Epinard on August 26, 1785 is graphically charted. Arrows (lower right) indicate thunderstorm.*

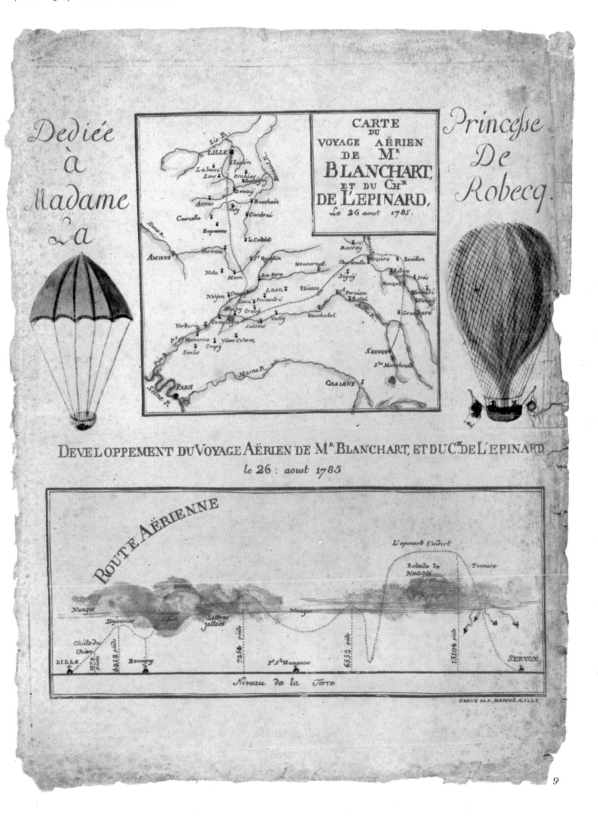

Dediée à Madame La

Princeſse De Robecq.

CARTE DU VOYAGE AËRIEN DE M. BLANCHART, ET DU Cℎ DE L'EPINARD, Le 26 aoust 1785.

DEVELOPPEMENT DU VOYAGE AËRIEN DE Mℝ BLANCHART, ET DU Cℂ DE L'EPINARD, le 26 : aoust 1785

ROUTE AËRIENNE

Niveau de la Terre

10

10 *Fanciful flying ship of 1783, year in which the first balloons took to the air. Need for steering free balloons was quickly realized, but methods tried, as here, came usually from the sea.*
11 *Gaily colored hybrid balloon, hydrogen at top, hot-air in the neck, caused death of first aeronaut Pilâtre de Rozier in 1785, when it caught fire during cross-Channel attempt.*

11

12 Horseman sails aloft in
1798. By this time balloon
exhibitions had become
elaborate.
13 Peak of exhibiting came
after 1850 when Paris
Hippodrome featured ascents by
the great aeronaut, Eugène
Godard, shown here with
unusual five-balloon assembly.
Rival Poitevin family featured
horsemen and ballerinas
suspended beneath huge
balloons.

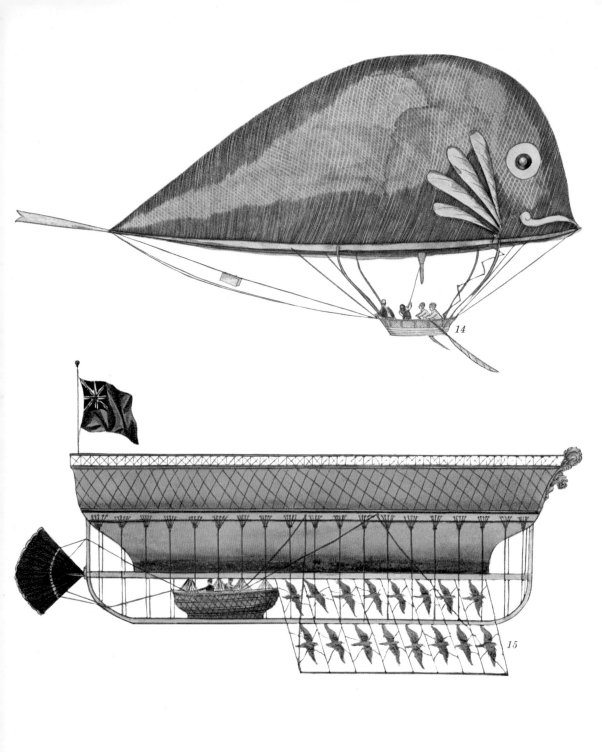

14

15

16

actually way ahead of his time, for the next really successful application of a motor to an airship did not take place for 30 years. In the meantime, Dupuy de Lôme, in 1872, completed a great airship originally projected for the siege of Paris—but its huge propeller was cranked by eight men, suitably fortified with rum ! In the same year Paul Haenlein of Germany experimented with a weak internal combustion engine attached to a captive dirigible. Finally, in the 1880's, when electricity was just coming to the fore, the Tissandier brothers built and flew a successful electric dirigible. But the first fully controllable airship, also powered by electricity, was *La France*, designed by Captains Charles Renard and Arthur Krebs with a heavy, eight horsepower electric motor fed by storage batteries. In 1884 *La France* defied the winds at last by making a perfect circuit from its starting point and back again.

The dirigible came of age with Santos-Dumont and Count von Zeppelin, both of whom applied internal combustion engines to their ships. Alberto Santos-Dumont, a lively, diminutive and very rich Brazilian of French extraction, who flew both dirigibles and the first successful airplane in France, was one of the most popular inventors of all time. Starting in 1898, he experimented with some 15 small, nonrigid dirigibles, all fitted with gasoline engines, and on October 19, 1901 ran one of them from St. Cloud around the Eiffel Tower and back within 30 minutes to win the Henri Deutsch prize of 100,000 francs, which he promptly distributed to his workmen and the poor of Paris. Santos-Dumont's frequent flights over the rooftops of Paris, his equally frequent accidents, none of them serious, his spirit and generosity endeared him to the French. His exploits were of incalculable importance in creating a new enthusiasm for aeronautics.

The courageous and determined Count Ferdinand von Zeppelin, a retired cavalry officer who had acquired his interest in balloons during the American Civil War, was equally popular in Germany, having been rescued a number of times from financial disaster by state lotteries, which were enthusiastically subscribed to by the German public. From the 1870's on he made a systematic study of the rigid airship—a series of balloons enclosed within a rigid, covered framework. Although Zeppelin was solely responsible for the successful development of the rigid dirigible, he owed much to two of his compatriots. The first successful application of a gasoline engine to an airship was accomplished by Dr. Wolfert in 1896 and 1897, while in the latter year an Austrian engineer, Schwartz, constructed the first rigid dirigible.

The Count's *Zeppelin No. 1*, during her first trials in 1900, executed sweeping circles above Lake Constance at speeds up to 20 miles per hour, then landed without mishap. This pioneer ship, 384 feet long, embodied the essential elements of all later Zeppelins, including such magnificent ships as the *Graf Zeppelin* and the *Hindenburg*. Despite a number of serious accidents (though none were fatal until 1913) Count von Zeppelin persisted, and by 1914 had constructed 25 dirigibles. One became Germany's first military airship in 1908; another flew from Lake Constance to Berlin in 1909 with the inventor on board and was received with boundless enthusiasm not only by the Emperor and Empress but by the entire population of the capital. In 1910, under the direction of the Count's assistant, Dr. Hugo Eckener, the *Deutschland* began the world's first scheduled passenger service.

During the early years of the twentieth century dirigibles of all types, rigid, semirigid and nonrigid, were operated in most of the larger countries of Europe. France, as always, was pre-eminent. Its highly successful *Lebaudy*, for instance, accomplished the first extensive aerial voyage with a gasoline engine in 1903. *La Patrie*, built for the French army in 1906, was lost over the Atlantic the following year, but was replaced by the 190-foot *Ville de Paris*, generously donated by Henri Deutsch de la Meurthe. The thriving French dirigible industry constructed many airships for continental countries as well as for England, Russia, and the United States, including the *America*, built for the American arctic explorer, Walter Wellman.

England's first dirigible was the inappropriately-named *Nulli Secundus*, a rather crude military training ship built by Colonel Capper and the American aeronaut, S. F. Cody, in 1907. The United States, lagging far behind, built few dirigibles worth mentioning, except perhaps for those of Thomas Scott Baldwin, one of which became the army's first airship in 1908. All of Baldwin's 13 airships were fitted with the efficient gasoline engines built by Glenn Curtiss, America's pioneer aviator.

Dirigibles were in the ascendant in this period, but the nonmotorized spherical balloon, which had ushered in the age of flight, still yielded prime sport for the wealthy and adventurous,

until the dangers of an increasingly industrialized landscape and the ascendancy of the airplane drastically restricted its use. Among free-balloon enthusiasts, "Hares and Hounds" races were popular, as well as the annual Gordon Bennett cup race. Captive balloons continued to perform at fairs, while high-altitude balloons were occasionally sent up to investigate the upper atmosphere.

But the days of the free balloon were numbered. Dirigibles, however, appeared to be firmly established as the safest and most efficient form of air transportation. Zeppelin's magnificent airships, with their roomy, luxurious passenger cabins lined with rosewood and mahogany, their sumptuous meals on high, their effortless flight, seemed to have solved the problem of air travel for the foreseeable future. These great ships, which could carry 20 or more passengers in comfort at speeds exceeding 40 miles per hour, were fast becoming the skyliners of the world. And it was obvious that the dirigible, too, would play an important part as a bombing machine in any future war.

It would have been hard to believe, in those years before World War I, that in scarcely a few decades the dirigible, and the free balloon too, would be rendered almost obsolete by that ugly duckling, the airplane, now just beginning to hop uncertainly off the ground. The development of a practical engine had made the dirigible a success. Ironically, the gasoline engine, again, was about to do the same for the heavier-than-air machine. It was the airplane, not the balloon in any of its guises, that was destined to give mankind a whole new dimension of flight.

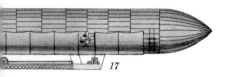

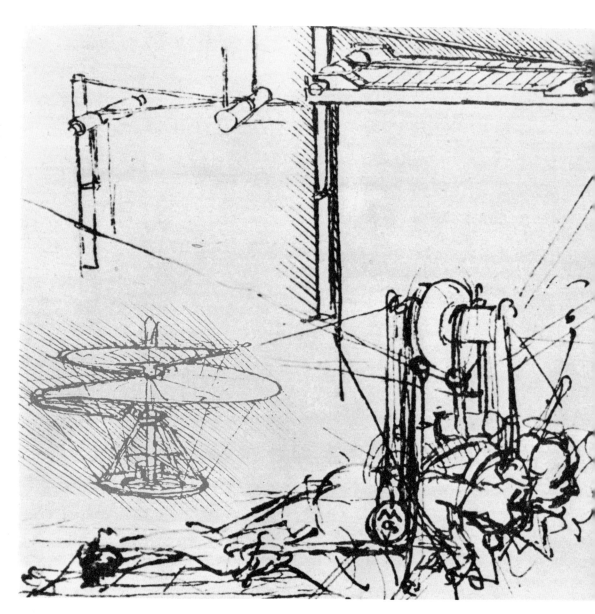

19 Sketches by Leonardo da Vinci, the "universal genius," for a flying machine to be activated by ropes, pulleys—and human muscle. Da Vinci studied many aspects of flight, including the helicopter (sketch at left).

"How strongly have the clouds, sweeping high over my head through the sky, tempted me to travel with them to foreign lands!" wrote Goethe, epitomizing man's age-old dream of navigating the "ocean of the air" on wings of his own design. The origins of human flight are shrouded in the mists of time. The many winged gods and flying legends of the ancients would seem to have little relevance to the story —with the possible exception of the poignant myth of Icarus, which symbolizes with such clarity the exaltation and the tragedy of man's persistent dream of flight. Authentic examples of human attempts to fly emerge only sparsely from early literature. Suetonius reports the fatal crash of a birdman at one of Nero's sumptuous festivals. A winged Saracen is supposed to have jumped to his death in the presence of a Byzantine emperor. Through the ages other brave birdmen flapped and died because they knew nothing of the principles of flight. As late as 1742 the aged Marquis de Bacqueville "a man who was a little crazy but who had lots of spirit," launched himself from the roof of his "hotel" across the Seine, landing on a washerwoman's barge on the other side. He broke his hip, but he did get across.

Even after serious experimentation had begun, in the early nineteenth century, it is astonishing to find how long it took to get a practical airplane into the air and keep it there, in sustained and controlled flight. As Octave Chanute once pointed out in the years before the Wrights, the man who was to make a success of the airplane would have to combine in himself something of the visionary inventor, the engineer, the mechanic, the mathematician

20　　　　　　　　　21

and, hopefully, the financier—to provide the wherewithal for his experiments. The airplane, being by definition a heavier-than-air machine, could not be expected, like the balloon, to be held in the sky by hot air or hydrogen. Power was required to lift it up, speed to keep it going, and skill to fly it. Thus the airplane had to be designed all of a piece, with every part contributing to the grand result—or once launched it would come down again, and almost certainly in more than one piece. These obvious facts go far to explain why the flying machine took so much longer to develop than the lighter-than-air balloon.

Then there was the all-important factor of the "state of the art." In the history of heavier-than-air flight certain great experimenters stand out—Leonardo da Vinci, George Cayley, Alphonse Pénaud—men who were eminently capable of solving the problem but whose attempts were doomed to failure because one or another of the elements necessary for successful flight had not yet reached the practical stage. And there was a host of lesser experimenters, each one of whom had grasped some part of the truth but had failed to perceive the rest. Some of them were theorists while others believed in the trial-and-error method. All of these—the

obscure figures along with the great names— contributed something to the advancement of the art of flying. But the final, grand result would have to wait until every piece of the jigsaw puzzle was ready to be fitted into a single pattern. This was accomplished by the Wright brothers, building upon all that had gone before.

Of the great experimenters, Leonardo da Vinci is the most interesting. As in so many other fields, his sketches and brief treatises on aeronautics—compiled in an age of morions and halberds—attest to the extraordinary genius of the man. His study of bird flight, including, as he wrote, "the almost imperceptible movements which preserve equilibrium," was intensive. "A bird is an instrument working according to mathematical law," he concluded, "which instrument it is within the capacity of man to reproduce with all its movements." His sketches of flapping-wing machines, of an airplane based on the wing structure of the bat, of helicopters and parachutes, are remarkable for the fact that they were realizable strictly within the materials available to him in the sixteenth century— wood, reed, metal, cloth, and rope. Leonardo did, however, overestimate the strength and endurance of human muscle, despite his many

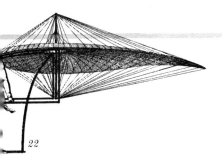

22

23

24

ingenious applications of rope and pulley devices. It is not known whether he actually experimented with his large machines, but he apparently was able to fly a little helicopter with some success.

Between Leonardo and the late eighteenth century there is little to report, except perhaps for the determined efforts of a seventeenth-century locksmith called Besnier, who tried to beat his way through the air with four hinged flaps on rods, activated by his arms and legs. In 1781, just before Pilâtre de Rozier's first flight, the great balloonist Blanchard experimented with a helicopter and a "flying ship" with four huge flapping wings, both full size. The helicopter may have flown. Naturally the triumphant success of Montgolfier and Charles with their balloons gave a great impetus to aeronautical experiments of all kinds. But heavier-than-air flight was a harder nut to crack than ballooning. Among other tentative efforts it is worth recalling the Swiss watch-maker, Jacob Degen, who flapped away in a crude flying machine, which he slung beneath a small balloon, between 1806 and 1817. With the French preoccupied with the balloon, the center of heavier-than-air research moved over to England, where it was to be dominated for

half a century by Sir George Cayley. Many years later Orville Wright wrote of Cayley that he "knew more of the principles of aeronautics than any of his predecessors, and as much as any that followed him up to the end of the nineteenth century." A practical designer as well as a theoretician of the first rank, Cayley belonged to that remarkable group of English-men—among them James Watt and George Stephenson—who laid the foundations for the industrial and technological revolution of the eighteenth and nineteenth centuries.

As early as 1809, Cayley had precisely defined the central problem of heavier-than-air flight : "to make a surface support a given weight by the application of power to the resistance of the air." Cayley also defined the fundamentals of the airplane : the curvature and angle of the wings, lateral and horizontal controls, the need for streamlining to reduce resistance to the air, the propeller, the advantages of combining lightness with strength, and of the biplane wing. Cayley even foresaw the use of the internal combustion engine. By 1808 he had developed and was testing a glider as big as a World War II fighter. His coachman, the story goes, was forced by his master to take one ride on the machine but refused to go up again, pointing

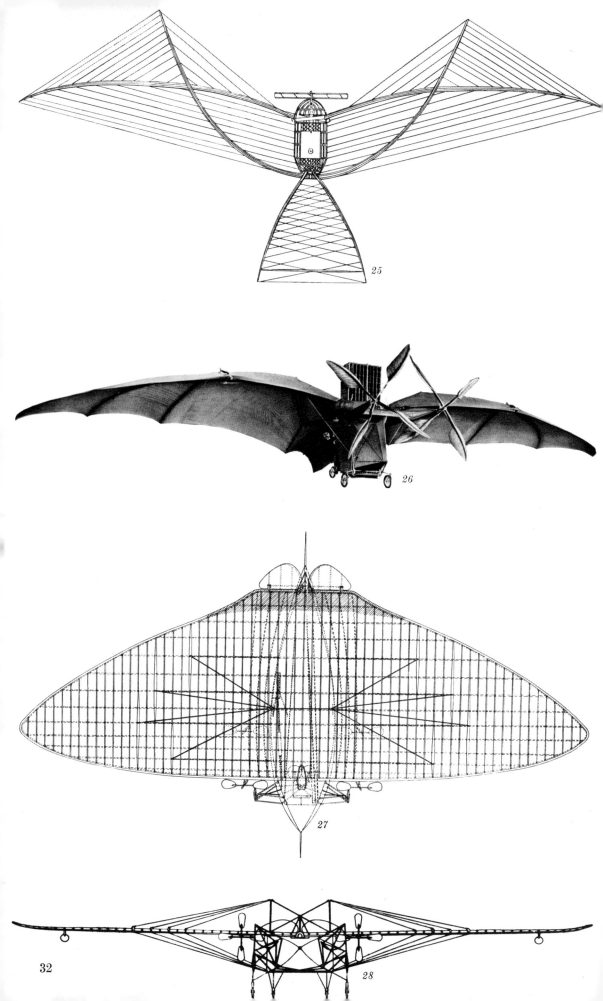

25 *Drawing for a full-scale airplane, patented by Félix du Temple in 1857 but never built. It was one of the first serious projects of the kind.*
26 *Clément Ader's "Avion No. 3," powered by two steam engines, was built with army backing, made a poor showing in 1897. His bat-wing "Eole" of 1890 flew better but lacked any semblance of control.*
27 *Alphonse Pénaud, one of the great theoreticians of his day, patented plans for an amphibian plane in 1876, but committed suicide when he failed to find backing for it.*
28 *Front view of Pénaud's plane, showing its advanced design.*
29 *Alphonse Pénaud.*
30 *Clément Ader.*

out that he had been hired to drive, not to fly. Throughout his long life Cayley continued his researches into aeronautics, both heavier and lighter than air, publishing in 1843 an unusual plan for a helicopter-like "converti-plane" which, with adequate power, might well have flown. This grand old man of aeronautics died in 1857, in his 84th year.

One direct result of Cayley's work was William Henson's astonishing "Aerial Steam Carriage," patented in 1842, a huge monoplane of practical design with a 150-foot wingspread and two six-bladed, 20-foot propellers powered by a 25-horsepower steam engine. The whole project was worked out in meticulous detail. Publishing hundreds of colored prints of the machine in flight, Henson tried to interest Parliament and the public in forming an "Aerial Steam Transit Company" to operate his contraption over world-wide air routes. With the mechanic, John Stringfellow, Henson actually constructed a 20-foot model of the machine. But his imagination had outrun his public. Derided for his fancies, he lost heart and exiled himself in America. Stringfellow there-after carried on alone. Designing a superb, lightweight steam engine, he fitted it in 1848 to a 10-foot model based on Henson's ideas that may well (although many dispute the fact) have achieved the first free flight of a powered air-plane. Launched from a wire, it is supposed to have flown as far as 120 feet.

About mid-century the school founded by Cayley lost its momentum. Another half century of experimentation, most of it on the continent, culminated in the first successful heavier-than-air flight. That this should have been accomplished by two Americans rather than by one Frenchman was really not surpris-ing, because the Wright brothers had profited in their experiments from everything of impor-tance that had been accomplished both in England and on the continent.

In the meantime, however, experimentation was aimed in several different directions. There were those who believed in experimenting with miniature models. There were others who tried to blunder into the air with enormous powered machines, with little regard to the conse-quences. Others took off in gliders, concentrat-ing upon the art of control while in the air. Many experimented with helicopters, particu-larly the Italian, Enrico Forlanini, whose steam-powered helicopter reached a height of 41 feet in free flight in 1877.

This was the period of giant captive balloons and of the first dirigibles. It was the period of Jules Verne, whose romances featured flying machines of many types. It was a period of vast hopes and discouraging progress, in which everything seems to have been tried and little accomplished. Most spectacular but of least importance were the attempts to launch full-scale machines, like the 1857 glider of Jean-Marie le Bris which, mounted on a cart pulled by a horse, unexpectedly jerked the inventor 300 feet into the air. Many of these worthy experimenters seemed afraid to fly, as if they knew that their machines, for all their size, were uncontrollable in flight. Louis-Pierre Mouillard, for instance, was thoroughly scared when one of his gliders gave him an unpremeditated ride in Algeria in 1865. More than ten years later Victor Tatin gingerly tested his compressed air

  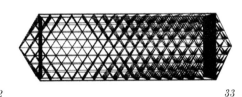

31 32 33

plane by flying it on a rope. Relying on sheer power, the large steam airplanes of Moy and Schill in England in 1875 and of Mozhaisky in Russia in 1882 apparently got off the ground. It is remarkable indeed how many airplanes of all types actually flew during the nineteenth century, but never for more than the briefest of uncontrolled flights.

But these essays were of little importance compared to the theoretical work of the period which, bit by bit, widened the knowledge of the mechanisms of flight. It was more often the studies of these inventors, rather than their experiments in the air, that helped eventually to make flight possible. It is a question, for instance, whether the steam-powered model of Félix du Temple, which may have been the first to leave the ground under its own power, was more important than the detailed patent plans he published in 1857 for a full-scale machine that he never built. Mouillard, he of the Algerian glider, who unsuccessfully tinkered with airplanes all his life, published *The Empire of the Air* in 1881, which became an aeronautical classic. Charles Renard, designer of the dirigible *La France* and a scientific genius, accomplished little of a practical nature in heavier-than-air flight ; yet the idea of the aileron as a means of

lateral control first appeared in his ten-winged glider-model as well as in the work and plans of Mouillard and others.

Head and shoulders above the rest stands the brilliant and tragic figure of Alphonse Pénaud, whose researches into aeronautics and bird flight—as well as his practical achievements—had a profound influence upon his own and later generations. He was responsible for recovering and publicizing the work of Cayley, while on his own he published in 1872 and 1873 an analysis of the laws of gliding, and later defined the three basic problems of flight : resistance of the air, resistance of the machine, and a light motor. Pénaud was consciously preparing himself to solve the enigma of heavier-than-air flight. He spent much time studying the suitability of cloth, metal, and wood for aerial constructions. In 1870 he invented the twisted rubber motor for experimental models and with it produced a miniature helicopter (which was later turned into a very popular toy), a mechanical flying bird, and a little model airplane, the *Planophore* which in numerous successful flights—some as long as 180 feet—demonstrated conclusively that sustained flight could be achieved. His life's work went into his detailed plans for a tailless amphibian plane, complete with retract-

35

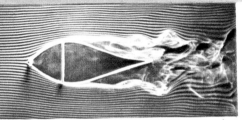

34

36

able landing gear, unified controls, and launching catapult, which he patented, with Paul Gauchot, in 1876. But the effort to gain support for building it was too much for him—he was not made for the rough-and-tumble of business —and he began to show signs of serious instability. He broke relations with an aeronautical society, of which he had been a most enthusiastic member. In 1880, when even the great Giffard refused to help him, he went home, locked up all his work (somewhat gruesomely) in a little coffin, and committed suicide. He was only thirty years old.

Following Pénaud there was a rash of miniature, rubber-propelled models. Another idea of Pénaud's was taken up by Etienne-Jules Marey, who worked out a method of studying bird flight and the flow of air currents through stop-photography. But in the period just before the Wrights the main line of aeronautical research diverged sharply in two directions. The experimenters with big machines hurled themselves more desperately than ever at the air, but their costly attempts added little to the progress of aviation. Motors of various types were now beginning to approach the weight-to-power ratio that would make powered flight a possibility. The steam engine, of course, which had proved so useful in ships and locomotives, was the most advanced at the time. Thus when Clément Ader's *Eole*, an intricately and beautifully constructed machine with adjustable wings modeled on the bat, made a tentative flight in a private park in 1890, it was powered by a lightweight, two-cylinder steam engine. The *Eole*, however, exhibited no semblance of control. Nevertheless, Ader tried again in 1897 with his two-engined *Avion No. III*, this time backed by the French army, but the results were equivocal and the army dropped him. Embittered, Ader destroyed all his work except *Avion No. III*, which still exists.

In England Sir Hiram Maxim, inventor of the machine gun, tried to fly in 1894 with his huge, many-winged *Multiplane*, which was mounted on tracks and powered by an enormous steam engine. When the machine began to take off the dismayed inventor, realizing that he would not be able to control it, throttled down the engine and called it a day. The experience of Samuel P. Langley, Secretary of the Smithsonian Institution at Washington, was somewhat different. In 1896 he actually achieved several long flights with his steam-driven model, but when, with government backing and much publicity, he tried twice in 1903 to launch a full-scale, man-carrying version of his *Aerodrome* from a houseboat on the Potomac River, he too met with dismal failure. To what extent, if any, his machine would have been controllable if it had flown, is still a matter of controversy. But it was powered by a remarkable radial gasoline engine which anticipated the future. And Langley's last and most decisive failure is chiefly remembered because it preceded, by less than two weeks, the first powered flight of the Wright brothers at Kitty Hawk.

Far more propitious for the future was the gliding school of the 1890's, led by the great Otto Lilienthal, who believed in learning to fly by actual practice in the air. Once control had been achieved, power could be added to the machine. This of course was opposite to the method employed by the advocates of the big machines. "In free flight in the air," Lilienthal wrote, "a large number of phenomena appear which the experimenter encounters nowhere else ; in particular, those relating to the wind must be taken into consideration in the construction and use of flying machines. The way in which we experience the irregularities of the wind while gliding through the air cannot be learned in any other way except by being in the air itself. . . ."

Making over 2,000 flights from hillsides and housetops, Lilienthal brought his gliders, which were made of cotton-covered bamboo and cane, to a high state of perfection. He was able to soar, sometimes reaching heights greater than his starting point, and to make turns. Indeed, the skill and daring of his flying, studied around the world through photographs, was of in-

calculable influence in encouraging and inspiring his fellow enthusiasts. An actual witness of Lilienthal's flights, who was impressed with the "precision with which he maneuvered his apparatus," wrote : "The spectacle of a man, supported on huge white wings, moving at a great height above us with the speed of a race horse, while the wind made a most peculiar humming sound in the cords of his apparatus, produced an impression on me which I shall never be able to forget."

Lilienthal died in 1896, after he had fallen from one of his gliders from a height of 50 feet. In his last years he had been flying biplanes with great success, and was about ready to equip the latest one with a small motor to agitate the ends of its wings (he did not believe in propellers). Lilienthal's English follower, Percy Pilcher, who lost his life, too, in an accident in September 1899, was also planning to add an engine of his own design to his most successful glider, the *Hawk*. Either one of these pioneers might well have achieved powered flight before the Wrights. Others of the gliding school were not far behind. Octave Chanute, an American citizen of French birth and another follower of Lilienthal, was one of the most engaging personalities of the period. With the help of two assistants, since he was too old to fly, he experimented with biplane gliders along the shores of Lake Michigan and eventually became the confidant and adviser of the Wright brothers in their momentous experiments. In far-off Australia the great technician, Lawrence Hargrave, developed the box-kite, which was to have a profound influence upon early French airplane design.

38   *39*   *40*

A significant measure of control in the air had been achieved, especially by Lilienthal. The gasoline engine had been perfected (the radial engine, for instance, designed by Manley for Langley's *Aerodrome* was far more advanced than that used by the Wrights). It was obvious to many that powered flight was at hand ; and indeed the pieces of the jigsaw puzzle were about to be put together. The Wright brothers, Orville and Wilbur, belonged to the school of Lilienthal. "My own active interest in aeronautical problems," Wilbur wrote in 1901, "dates back to the death of Lilienthal in 1896. The brief notice of his death which appeared in the telegraphic news at that time aroused a passive interest which had existed from my childhood."

The brothers were influenced, too, by Chanute, not only through the warm interest he took in their work but through his book, *Progress in Flying Machines*, which summed up the aeronautical knowledge of the period. As children, the Wrights had been fascinated with a Pénaud helicopter, brought to them by their father as a toy. Later they studied not only the writings of Pénaud and Lilienthal, but also those of Cayley, Mouillard, Marey, and many others. And they profited from the mistakes of men like Langley

and Maxim. In their careful, painstaking way they reviewed the entire experience of heavier-than-air experimentation, drew the proper conclusions, and then contributed some ideas of their own—proved out, in the manner of Lilienthal, by direct experience in the air. The Wrights were not pioneers. Their work, rather, culminated a century of experience.

The Wright brothers began their serious study of aeronautics in 1899, when they wrote to the Smithsonian Institution at Washington for literature on heavier-than-air flight. At this time they were running a bicycle works in Dayton, Ohio, which provided them with a machine shop for their experiments. Soon deep in a study of the principles of aeronautics, they decided that control and stability in the air was the crucial factor, and in a few months had worked out their method of maintaining lateral equilibrium by "warping" the ends of the wings with wires. This in itself was an advance on Lilienthal, who maintained equilibrium by adjusting his body and legs in flight. After building a biplane glider, the brothers tested it in 1900 at Kitty Hawk, North Carolina—chosen for its prevailing winds—either from a hill, with one of them as a passenger, or at the end of a rope. It proved quite successful.

 41

 42

Encouraged, they built another glider, almost twice as large as any ever constructed by their predecessors, and tested it, again at Kitty Hawk, in the spring of 1901. To their surprise, it proved most difficult to fly. Something seemed to be wrong with their calculations.

In a fit of despondency, Wilbur told his brother he didn't think man would fly in a thousand years. But Chanute, who had been at Kitty Hawk, urged the Wrights on. Back in Dayton the brothers studied the problem. They constructed two wind tunnels and tested some 200 different wing shapes, reaching the conclusion at last that most of the data supplied by their predecessors was in error. In 1902 they returned once more to Kitty Hawk with a new glider, based upon their own calculations. Fitted with a single control, which operated both a new, movable tail and the lateral warping of the wings, this glider proved itself in flight quite ready for an engine. Provision of a light-weight, gasoline engine was no problem, but to construct an efficient propeller required months of tedious calculations. Finally, in the autumn of 1903, they returned to Kitty Hawk. On December 17—it was a cold, windy morning—the plane was brought out and the engine started. Orville lay down in the pilot's cradle. Released,

the machine moved forward on its track with Wilbur steadying one wing, then lifted into the air some ten feet, darted downwards again, then flew uncertainly through the air for about 100 feet before it settled to the ground.

"This flight lasted only 12 seconds," Orville wrote later, "but it was nevertheless the first in the history of the world in which a machine carrying a man had raised itself by its own power into the air in full flight, and sailed forward without reduction of speed, and had finally landed at a point as high as that from which it started." In these carefully qualified terms the Wrights underlined the real meaning of this most unspectacular of events. Their flight had been less dramatic than many of those attempted by the experimenters with big machines, they had spent far less money than either Professor Langley or Sir Hiram Maxim, they had not flown as far nor as high as Lilienthal; nevertheless they had proved the *possibility* of sustained, powered flight. The potential was there, as it had never been with the Aders, Langleys, and Maxims. To the Wrights this first tentative flight was but one incident in their relentless effort to develop a practical flying machine. But the world, in time, would learn to understand its importance.

43 *Henri Farman, in his Voisin plane, heads for Rheims in*
first cross-country trip. In 1908 France led world in flying.

The first successful flight in a heavier-than-air machine had been accomplished. It had lasted only 12 seconds. But for the first time the correct principles of flight—those principles that still govern the design of heavier-than-air craft today—had been not only discovered but applied. Success, the Wrights knew, was not to be measured in terms of power, nor even less in terms of merely being airborne. Success depended above all upon the ability to maintain stability and control while in the air—and this they had already achieved in their last glider. In sum, their major work had been accomplished long before their crude machine first bounced into the air at Kitty Hawk.

During the years immediately following their exploit little of consequence seemed to have occurred in the field of aeronautics. The quiet, however, was deceptive, for word of the Wrights' achievement had begun to leak out. Both before and after their first flight several detailed articles by Wilbur Wright and by Chanute had been published both in the United States and in France. As early as 1902, for instance, Captain Ferber of the French Army had experimented with a powered glider, "du type Wright," hung from a crane. Then in September of 1906 the indefatigable Santos-Dumont, who owed nothing to the Wrights but the incentive, managed to hop a few feet in his ungainly *14-bis*, a tail-first biplane that combined features from Hargrave's kites with ideas proposed by Cayley. By November he had covered 720 feet in 21 1/5 seconds. Europe, already in love with the little Brazilian, wildly acclaimed his flights.

The Wrights, however, had not been inactive. Moving their operations from Kitty Hawk to Dayton in 1904, they constructed a new machine, rented a 68-acre cow pasture called "Huffmann's Prairie," and methodically proceeded to learn to fly. In all they flew 105 flights that year. In 1905, with an improved machine, they ended their flying season on October 5 with an incredible flight of nearly 25 miles in 38 minutes. Then for a period of two and a half years they flew no more. Their United States patent had not yet been granted, and they were determined to find a buyer for their invention before the world discovered their progress and began to imitate them. Twice during 1905 they had approached the United States government, only to be turned down in terms that were downright insulting. The Wrights' misguided policy of secrecy was, in fact, damaging their cause. In September of 1907, announcing a prize for a flight of one kilometer, the *Scientific American* magazine noted that the Wrights claimed they had solved the problem of flight. But "no public demonstration has ever been made by them," the magazine pointed out, and "still many people doubt this." Not many persons, few of them experts, had seen the Wrights fly, and aeronautical enthusiasts in Europe, now growing more proficient with their machines, began to ask, "Are they fliers or liars?"

On July 4, 1908, at Hammondsport, New York, the *Scientific American* trophy was won by Glenn Curtiss with a flight of 6,000 feet, carried out in a blaze of publicity. Curtiss, who was to become the Wrights' greatest American competitor, was a self-taught builder and racer of motorcycles who in 1907 had joined Alexander Graham Bell, the inventor of the telephone, and three other young men in an aeronautical group, rather grandly called The Aerial Experiment Association. Each of the four younger members had been responsible for the design and construction of a plane. The first flew, lamely, in March of 1908, the second in May. By far the most successful of these planes was Curtiss's *June Bug*, in which he had won the *Scientific American* trophy. Commenting on Curtiss's flight, that magazine noted, " . . . it is probable that after further practice . . . he will be able to duplicate the performances of Delagrange and Farman."

The airplane was invented in America, but aviation came of age in France. Taking the lead from gallant Santos-Dumont, her aviators one by one clambered shakily into the air. Blériot and Farman, Delagrange and Esnault-Pelterie, Voisin and Latham—they were a dashing crew, handsome and spirited as the graceful monoplanes that so many of them flew. These men were sportsmen, and yet mechanics too, for it was the age of the bicycle and of automobile rallies. Money was easy, business was good, and fortunes were not hard to make. Blériot's fortune, gained from an automobile headlight, went into his flying. Henri Farman had been a champion cyclist and automobile racer before he turned to flying. He was an artist too, and Delagrange a sculptor. Indeed, there was something of the artist in all of these men, seeking the lift of danger, the excitement of a new dimension. It was the French who first dramatized the beauty and zest of flying before the world.

Well before Santos-Dumont's flight, Gabriel and Charles Voisin had been experimenting with a boxlike glider that owed much to Hargrave's kites. Louis Blériot could not seem to get a powered version of the Voisin biplane off the ground, but early in 1907 he turned to monoplanes and thereafter made flight after flight, soon exceeding Santos-Dumont's record. Later in the year Robert Esnault-Pelterie began to fly in a rival monoplane of his own design, while Léon Delagrange and Henri Farman started their careers in boxlike Voisins. But it was the monoplane —gracefully designed and bearing graceful names like *Libellule* and *Antoinette*—that seemed to embody the French spirit in aviation. Blériot's were the first to fly. With a species of aileron, "joy-stick" control, wheeled landing gear and propeller up front, they anticipated the design of the future.

Blériot had already made several flights when Wilbur Wright came to Europe in 1907 to negotiate with a number of interested governments, including the French. The Wrights still refused to fly until they had realized their ambition to set up an international flying business based on their patents. But time was growing short. In January of 1908 Farman won the Deutsch-Archdeacon prize for the first official flight of over one kilometer. In February the Wrights' bid for the first American military plane had been accepted. In March, while the Wrights were signing a contract with the French, creating a syndicate licensed to manufacture and sell Wright planes in France, Farman raced Delagrange for a mile and a quarter. The contract was signed just in time.

Since it called for demonstration flights, the Wrights began to fly once more, practicing quietly at Kitty Hawk in April before Wilbur returned to France.

In August, based near Le Mans, Wilbur began to fly, piling record upon record while he exhibited an ease of control and versatility that astounded the French. Generously, they began to idolize him. Blériot was quoted as saying, "The Wright machine is indeed superior to our airplanes." Early in 1909 manufacturing arrangements were worked out with Italy, and later with Germany and England. When Orville (who had come to join his brother) and Wilbur returned to the United States in June, they were received as heroes.

After Wilbur's triumph in Europe the already smoldering bonfire burst into bright flame. Europe went air-mad, as it had gone balloon-mad over a hundred years before. In England, strangely slow to catch the flying fever, American-born Colonel S.F. Cody made the first official flight in October 1908 (though in June A.V. Roe, founder of the great Avro Company, had unofficially hopped into the air in a biplane of his own design). Between January and September 1909 the first official flights were made in Germany, Russia, and Italy. Spreading from France and the United States, flying was becoming international. It was time to cross some water, to fly from country to country.

Gallant Hubert Latham, who had taken up aviation because his doctors had given him only a year to live, tried twice to cross the English Channel in his *Antoinette*, but failed both times. Blériot, who also had designs on the Channel, rushed to beat Latham. Hobbling

45 Prize-winning flight of Glenn Curtiss's "Gold Bug" in 1909. The American pioneer first flew in 1908.

46 American county fair poster from the pioneer period of aviation. Stunt-flying and air meets popularized flying, helped to cover expenses.

47 Blériot's successful Channel crossing in 1909 gave boost to aviation. Here Father Neptune hangs himself in contemporary German cartoon.

48 Rare photograph of Blériot, about time of Channel feat.

49 Special edition of "Le Matin" announces Blériot's crossing.

50 Poster for 1910 air meet at Nice in France. The first great air meet was held at Rheims in August of 1909, setting the pattern for many others in Europe and America during the next few years.

46

47

48

49

MEETING D'AVIATION
NICE
10=25 AVRIL 1910
P.L.M.

BILLETS D'ALLER & RETOUR
INDIVIDUELS & DE FAMILLE A PRIX RÉDUITS
TRAINS EXTRA-RAPIDES DE JOUR & DE NUIT
CH. BSOR

into his monoplane with a leg still bandaged from a recent accident (he was famous for his accidents), he took off over the water on July 25, 1909. Soon he had lost his bearings. "For ten minutes or so I was alone," he wrote, "isolated, lost in the middle of the foamy sea. . . . Those ten minutes seemed long to me, and I was really happy to see . . . a grey line emerging from the sea. . . . It was the English coast." Later he flew along the cliffs near Dover, looking for a landing place. "A craggy bit of coast comes into view on my right, a moment before the castle of Dover. A mad joy comes over me. I turn in this direction, I plunge ahead. I am over land !" Crashing bumpily in a meadow behind the castle, Blériot stepped out on English soil. The whole world thrilled to his exploit.

The flying frenzy reached its peak in August, a month after Blériot's crossing of the Channel, when the best planes and most dashing pilots of the day came together at Rheims to exhibit their skill before a brilliant international audience. This first of the great air meets not only confirmed France's lead in aeronautics but provided an enormous stimulus to aircraft design and manufacturing. Thirty-eight planes of all types took part, and a week of spectacular flying showed the world how far and how fast aviation had developed. Each day new records were made and old ones surpassed. Farman flew a continuous 118.06 miles, breaking Wilbur Wright's recent record. Latham won the altitude record at 500 feet, and set a speed record of 42 miles per hour over a 100-kilometer course. Glenn Curtiss (the lone American, since the Wrights refused to participate) unexpected-

ly triumphed over Blériot in the 20-kilometer course and became the hero of the hour. Both of them had flown at about 48 miles per hour, the fastest man had ever flown through the air.

Rheims put aviation on the map, and at Rheims the trends and developments in aviation for the next few years had their real beginning. Sooner or later, most of the great pioneers became aircraft manufacturers. As early as 1906 the Voisin brothers had set up what amounted to a factory to build their box-kite planes. By 1908 Farman and Esnault-Pelterie were in business, and Léon Levavasseur was manufacturing not only the famous *Antoinette* engine but also the *Antoinette* monoplane, both named for the charming daughter of his backer, Gastambide. In 1909, the year of Rheims, small manufacturing concerns sprouted everywhere, Blériot and Breguet in France, the Short brothers (building Wright planes under license) and Handley-Page in Britain, Etrich in Germany, and in the United States, first the Herring-Curtiss Company and then the Wright Company. Curtiss started his company with the patents of the Aerial Experiment Association, which he had inherited after its dissolution. The Wright Company, backed by a glittering group of wealthy Americans, was capitalized at $1,000,000.

International aviation, in the years before World War I, seems to present a bewildering picture of hazardous flights, foolhardy stunts, bigger and better air shows—and of all too many cruel deaths of young men and women. On closer view, however, one finds some sense in most of it. The air meets, for instance, which after Rheims were staged in profusion

51   Daring British aviator,
Claude Grahame-White, takes
off from Washington street
on October 14, 1910, after
enthusiastic welcome by high
government officials.

52 The stunt-flyer, Lincoln Beachey, often called "The Flying Fool,"
maneuvers his plane over Niagara Falls and under the bridge in June, 1911.
53 Stars of the show, Louis Paulhan of France and Glenn Curtiss, race their
planes over the grandstands at the Los Angeles air meet of 1910.

53

in every major flying country, were actually public testing grounds for the planes and pilots of competing manufacturers. The stunts and races were made for money or prizes, for (like everybody else) the flying people needed money to keep going. Some of the more daring stunts, like Pégoud's looping-the-loop and other acrobatics in a Blériot in 1913, were intended both to test and to advertise the capabilities of the manufacturers' planes. Other public flights were made in the interests of keeping the public airminded. Claude Grahame-White, for instance, toured England in a plane emblazoned with the message "Wake up England." The long-distance flights, like that of Roland Garros, who crossed the Mediterranean in 1913 without even a life preserver, or of Géo Chavez, who got across the Alps three years earlier but was killed at the end of the flight, were made for sheer prestige.

Prestige, too, was the reward of dashing Calbraith Rodgers, who raced across the United States in 1911 (in 68 hops, with 15 crashes and four rebuildings of the plane), only to arrive too late to win a $50,000 prize. It is harder to assess the motives of Lincoln Beachey, the "flying fool," who risked his life flying over Niagara Falls and under its bridge, or competed with Barney Oldfield in his racing car, skimming a few feet above the ground. During 1910 alone, 37 well-known aviators met their deaths. In 1913 Beachey quit flying, with a bitter blast against morbid crowds who were out for thrills, but resumed again and crashed to his own death two years later. Harriet Quimby, always exquisitely dressed in the air, suffered the same fate in 1912. Indeed, many daring women,

starting with France's Baronne de la Roche in 1909, took to flying. Aviation, always struggling against the apathy of the public and the conservatism of governments, needed all the support and publicity it could get. This, plus the sheer zest and excitement of flying, explains the whole bewildering epoch.

Governments, conservative as always, were slow to adopt the airplane as a military weapon. Although the United States took the lead, it soon fell far behind. In 1908, while Wilbur Wright was thrilling the French with his flying, Orville was demonstrating another machine before the U.S. Army at Fort Myer. In September his plane crashed, killing his passenger, young Lt. Selfridge, who became the first aviation fatality. A year later the tests were resumed, and on August 2, 1909, the Army accepted the world's first military airplane.

France began to think of military aviation a few months after the Wright plane had been accepted, and by January 1910 a few Blériots, Farmans, Antoinettes and Voisins were in service. Progress thereafter was steady, if not spectacular—steady enough to frighten France's ancient enemy, Germany, whose military aviation, also started in 1909, had been strangled by tight budgets. Resorting to public lotteries of the kind that had rescued Count von Zeppelin, the government began pouring money into aviation so that by the time the war started the military fleets of France and Germany were approximately equal and were the strongest in the world. England got a late start in 1910 with the purchase of a De Havilland plane, but thereafter made so little progress that by 1914 it had very few

54 Despite such experiments as this bomb release mechanism of about 1912, the airplane was not equipped for combat when World War I started.
55 Bombs were dropped by hand or released by such crude mechanisms as this. Until the machine gun proved its worth, pilots used small arms in combat.
56 Few planes were larger than this captured German " Taube, " displayed at the Invalides by the French.

54

55

military aircraft, and many of these were French. Italy was the first country to use the airplane in war. During a scrap with Turkey in 1911, six of its planes scouted the enemy lines and dropped a few bombs (hand grenades), terrifying the Turks and provoking press comment on the evils of air attack.

Water-based flying began with Henri Fabre's *Canard* of 1910, a weird contraption with three floats and cellular wings which nevertheless flew from the water with remarkable agility. The scene then shifted to America, where in 1911 the ingenious Glenn Curtiss worked out his own, more substantial version of a hydroplane. Laying siege to the Navy, Curtiss had one of his fliers land a plane on the deck of the U.S.S. *Pennsylvania* off the West Coast; then a month later himself landed in the water in a hydroplane next to the same warship. The Navy, convinced of the plane's usefulness, promptly created a flying service in July of 1911. The next year Curtiss, now the acknowledged world expert on water-based planes, created a true flying boat, and by 1914 had built a giant, twin-engined ship, the

America, intended for a transatlantic crossing, which had to be called off when the war began. In France Voisin's amphibian *Canard* was tested successfully on the Seine in 1911, and sold to the French Navy in 1912. By 1914 seaplanes were common in the naval establishments of Europe.

When the war broke out in 1914, the airplane was still a fragile fledgling only 11 years old, better suited to the county fair and the air meet than to the stern exigencies of war. But four years of war changed aviation beyond all recognition. The little workshops of the pioneer airmen turned into huge factories capable of producing, for the larger nations, 20 to 30,000 planes a year. The simple two-seater of 1914 evolved into mammoth bombers, fast scouts, and agile fighters. The air arm became a recognized branch of every military establishment. Yet after the war many still doubted the importance of military aircraft. It would take another world war to make the point.

At the war's opening the planes of all the combatants were roughly similar in their deficiencies. They were all small, weak, clumsy, and slow, and there was little differentiation between one type and another. None were armed, for the military mind, distrusting the airplane, had assigned it to reconnaissance alone. In this, however, it was so successful that soon all the belligerents were clamoring for more planes to help with scouting, aerial photography, and artillery spotting. At first hostile pilots waved amicably at each other as they passed in the air, then they took to shooting at each other with rifles, muskets, and revolvers. In time their planes were loaded down with a bizarre assortment of armaments, of which the machine gun proved to be the most efficient. When Roland Garros, the veteran French pilot, began shooting his machine gun through an armor-plated propeller, the Germans called in Anthony Fokker, the Dutch designer, who soon worked out a device synchronizing the gun with the propeller, which proved disastrous to Allied flyers until its secret was discovered.

Thus one achievement was capped by another. Fokker's original German fighter, which helped to prove the superiority of the tractor plane for speed and climb, was eventually outclassed by the French Nieuport. Fokker's answer was his triplane, which sacrificed other elements to rate of climb and maneuverability. With planes now capable of aerial dogfights, the "ace" came into his own. The exploits of von Richthofen, of Albert Ball, of Georges Guynemer, of Billy Bishop, and of Raoul Lufbery of the American volunteer Lafayette Escadrille, captured the imagination of the public. But the costly individual dogfights soon gave way to battles between formations, 20 to 30 on a side, practicing complex maneuvers first tried out by the stunt flyers before the war. In this type of combat, initiated by the "Red Knight," Baron von Richthofen, the flight commander became all-important. Richthofen himself was one of the best, until he was shot down in 1918—and buried with full military honors by his foes. So too, in the last year of the war, was the American flight commander, "Eddie" Rickenbacker. These men were heroes; but the loss in life among the aces was prohibitive.

The true heavy bomber, so prophetic for the future of aviation, did not make its appearance until the late years of the war. Bombing was practiced from the beginning, but the earliest bombs were often dropped by hand from conventional machines, and of course did very little damage. More serious were the Zeppelin attacks on England and France, which began soon after war was declared; but again these night raids were more terrifying than damaging, and the giant Zeppelins proved far too vulnerable to attack. By 1917 they were succeeded over London by the much-feared German twin-engined Gotha bomber which, with the rather similar Handley-Page and the large Caproni trimotors of Italy, marked the emergence of the specialized heavy bomber. The Germans experimented with enormous, multi-engined bombers, some with wingspans of 150 feet, while the Russians, thanks to Igor Sikorsky, had a fleet of four-engined machines. The plane commander's compartment in these huge ships almost suggested the bridge of an ocean liner.

Yet the bombing record of these monstrous planes was negligible. In fact until the very end of the war the practice of air bombardment was fumbling and ineffectual. The French never employed more than short-range, tactical bombing. The British consistently dispersed their forces over too many targets until, after the creation of the Royal Air Force in 1918, an Independent Air Force, stationed far behind the lines, bombed Germany concentratedly with some success. The Germans alone managed to concentrate their attacks throughout the war.

During the war, water-based aircraft, as well as a few blimps, operated in large numbers as naval auxiliaries off the coasts of Europe. The British specialized in heavy flying boats modelled on those of Curtiss while the Germans used speedy, short-range float planes. Neither, however, could operate far from shore. The British for a time launched land-based *Camel* fighters from lighters towed to sea, then in 1917 commissioned the first primitive aircraft carrier, the *Furious*, with an after-deck for retrieving its planes.

When the United States entered the war in 1917, France appealed for 4,500 planes and 5,000 pilots. The Americans, unprepared and totally inexperienced, hurriedly set up a huge aircraft program that soon bogged down in hopeless confusion. Only in the closing months of the war did it begin to furnish a fraction of the promised planes and pilots. Most notable contribution of the Americans was the Liberty engine, set in a British DH-4 airframe, and the Curtiss "Jenny" trainer.

Airpower as a whole achieved its full potential during the great St. Mihiel offensive of September 1918, when in the first mass air campaign in history nearly 1,500 planes of all types, under the command of the American General, "Billy" Mitchell, wrested control of the air from the Germans. Yet this first coordinated campaign was more like a rehearsal for the massive air campaigns of World War II. Aviation in all its forms—bombing, fighting, the use of scouts and seaplanes—was too new to make more than a tentative and incomplete impression upon the course of the first great war. The military value of airpower would be a controversial matter for many years to come.

58 Carcass of Zeppelin in
England, 1916. Bombers soon
replaced vulnerable airships.
59 German ace Boelcke, in
Fokker, destroys enemy fighter
over Verdun.

60   *Capacious interior of French Goliath bomber,*
converted for use as airliner soon after the war.
Despite comfort of such big planes, airlines
developed very slowly.

Military aviation had made prodigious strides during the war. The United States, for instance, which entered the conflict in 1917 with only 55 antiquated planes and a handful of inexperienced pilots, was capable at the time of the Armistice of turning out 21,000 planes a year from 24 aircraft plants, and its Air Service had grown to 20,000 officers and 170,000 men. But in no country, at the time of the Armistice, was there a single transport plane capable of carrying passengers in reasonable comfort.

At the end of the war the whole elaborate military structure was disbanded, almost overnight. Orders were cancelled, factories closed, pilots grounded. The swollen aircraft industry, abandoned to its fate, turned hopefully to the public, painting a rosy picture of a plane in every garage and fleets of airliners whisking passengers from New York to Washington, from Paris to London. But the man in the street showed little interest. He had thrilled from afar to the exploits of the wartime aces, but he was not going to risk his own neck in the primitive planes of the day. In dire straits, the aircraft industry faltered, especially in the United States. Many companies failed, others struggled on. As Anthony Fokker so sagely remarked, "Flying will be here to stay only when it ceases to be an adventure."

Commercial aviation did not develop in the United States for many years, but in Europe, with its shorter distances, the first tentative airlines appeared right after the war. The example was set by a military service that shuttled documents and personnel between London and Paris during the Peace Conference.

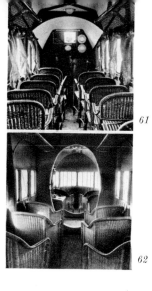

61

62

Soon a number of small private airlines, using crudely modified warplanes for lack of anything better, had struggled into being. The first was the German Luft-Reederei, which opened an airline between Berlin and Weimar in February of 1919. In the same month the Société Farman flew 13 passengers, including the great Henri Farman and his wife, from Paris to London in a giant converted Goliath bomber. A champagne lunch was served in flight. Less fortunate were the first passengers of the British Aircraft Transport and Travel Ltd., which opened a London to Paris service in August with small DH-9 bombers. Bundled into leather coats, helmets and goggles and squeezed into a tiny compartment, the passengers, as one author has put it, "could only sit and think how wonderful it was !" Seaplanes and all sizes of bombers—even the huge triplane Caproni, and the four-engined Handley-Page V/1500, built at the end of the war to bomb Berlin—were modified and pressed into service. Ornate interiors, light wicker seats, and the inevitable vases and window curtains were supposed to give the passengers a feeling of comfort and security : but the noise level on these ancient planes was almost unbearable ; the vibration was intense, the ride bumpy beyond belief, and the cabins draughty and cold. No wonder most travellers were content to use the trains and ships they knew so well.

Yet there was progress, thanks to far-sighted government support of the struggling airlines. The Dutch K.L.M., today the oldest airline continuously in existence, was formed in 1919 with government backing and staged its first flight from London to Amsterdam on May 17,

1920. By the beginning of 1921, thanks again to government subsidies, ten small airlines were operating in France. Several of these combined to form the Air Union in 1923 (which became Air France ten years later). In Belgium the government airline, Sabena, was also organized in 1923. At this time Croydon airport at London, handling up to 30 cross-Channel flights a day, had become a busy place. But the British airlines, hard-pressed by the French and with no government support, were in trouble. Belatedly, the government stepped in and in 1924 merged four shaky, independent airlines into the state-financed Imperial Airways. In the next year Germany's state-supported Deutsche Lufthansa, an outgrowth of the Luft-Reederei, was formed. With its excellent organization and fast, modern transports its paramilitary nature was hard to conceal. It soon became one of the most efficient airlines in Europe. Indeed, the day of the converted bomber was passing. Beginning with Germany's advanced, all-metal, low-wing Junkers transport of 1919 and Fokker's Dutch planes of succeeding years, more and more transports, designed expressly for passenger carrying, were entering into service.

The light plane suitable for flying clubs—the kind that would fit into a garage—developed slowly, although private flying always had its enthusiasts. By 1925 government encouragement and technical advances had made possible the enormously successful British Moth. The French Potez, German Klemm and the somewhat larger Stinson in the United States also became popular. Several Stinsons actually crossed the Atlantic.

61 *Fringed curtains, wicker chairs, speedometer and altimeter adorn interior of Imperial Airways W-10 liner.*
62 *Interior of French Farman transport, a converted twin-engined Goliath bomber. Pilot's cockpit was on roof of cabin.*
63 *Loading passengers for London. Interiors of early airliners were comfortable, but ride was bumpy, cold and noisy. Imperial Airways was formed by British government in 1924.*
64 *Pilot's cockpit in single-engined Fokker F-7A airliner, used by Dutch K.L.M. 1925-1939. Fokkers were much in demand.*

63

64

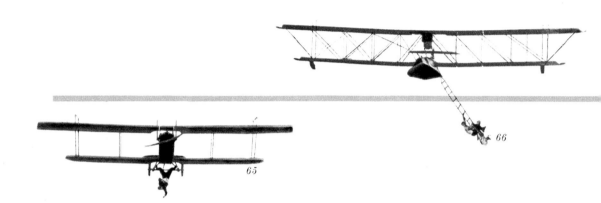

65

66

Until 1925 aviation in the United States was at a standstill. The public was not interested in private planes nor the government in airlines. There were no real airlines, except perhaps for a momentarily successful one which in 1920 flew thirsty Americans from Florida to Cuba to get a drink—for it was the prohibition era. Probably the "barnstormers" did more for the cause of aviation than anybody else. They flew for the love of it, and for the money they could get by stunting and wing-walking with their old surplus "Jennies" at county fairs. They took up countless people around the country for "joy hops"—and managed to communicate their enthusiasm to many. Some of the greatest flyers of later years came from their ranks.

Here and there dedicated designers and engineers went on planning the planes of the future. And in Washington the Post Office Department dreamed of a great national airmail service that would support and nurture commercial aviation in the country. The first airmail flights, linking New York and Washington, were staged in May of 1918. The next year the Post Office initiated a New York-to-Chicago run and in 1920 extended it to San Francisco by daylight. At night the mail was put on trains. A year later, when the

airmail appropriation from Congress was in doubt, ten brave pilots inaugurated day and night flights across the entire continent, in the dead of winter and without navigational aids, in order to dramatize the service. Their courage was expended in a good cause, for by 1924 the transcontinental route was lighted, and soon a few passengers were being carried with the mails.

America led in airmail, but in France, after 1919, a similar group of courageous, high-minded pilots, including the writer Saint-Exupéry, pioneered new airmail routes into Africa and across the Atlantic to South America. It was the heroic long-distance flights of the 1920's, however, that laid the basis for the international air routes of our day. As Sir Alan Cobham, British explorer of the Australian and African routes, once said, "My flights were not stunt flights ; they were demonstrations that flying journeys could be achieved with regularity and safety." The Atlantic, which was crossed four times in 1919, was the first great challenge. Of the three U.S. Navy Curtiss flying boats that made the first attempt in May, only one, the NC-4, managed to reach the Azores and from there flew to Lisbon and Plymouth. In June, two British officers (Alcock and Whitten-Brown), a dog, a cat, and a sack of mail made it

from Newfoundland to Ireland in a grossly overladen Vimy bomber, crashing safely into an Irish bog at the end. In the next month the British dirigible, R-34, crossed the Atlantic from Scotland to New York, then returned to England via the southern route. Four months later another Vimy bomber, piloted by Captain Ross Smith and a crew of three, charted one of the great Empire air lanes of the future with a 11,294-mile flight from England around the world to Australia.

These exploits were merely preliminary to the hundreds of great flights during the next two decades that opened up the air routes of the world. In 1923 the United States was spanned nonstop from east to west in a record 26 hours and 50 minutes by Lts. Macready and Kelly. Their plane was so heavily laden that it took 20 miles to reach an altitude of 400 feet. Next year two out of four Air Service "world cruisers" managed to circle the globe in 15 days of flight. The flights multiplied. The French explored North Africa, the British began to link their far-flung empire by air, two Portuguese flew the South Atlantic to Rio in 1922, and in 1925, the first flight from Belgium to the Belgian Congo was accomplished. One of the greatest of the air explorers—so akin in spirit to the sea-explorers of the Renaissance—was Sir Alan Cobham, who was knighted for his services. In later years, he reminisced, "The great attraction was the exploring aspect, the opening up of a territory new to me. . . What fascinated me was hitting up the next horizon."

Looking to the future, perhaps the most important explorations were those of the polar routes. In 1925 the Norwegian explorer, Roald Amundsen, and Lincoln Ellsworth, son of his backer, had almost reached the North Pole in two seaplanes. Next year, in the Italian dirigible *Norge*, piloted by Umberto Nobile, they tried again, reaching the Pole only a few days after the American, Lieutenant Commander Richard E. Byrd, had flown across it for the first time in his Fokker trimotor. Amundsen later lost his life in an effort to rescue Nobile, who had crashed in the Arctic in another airship. But Byrd went on to head his Antarctic expedition to "Little America" in 1929, during which he made the first flight over the South Pole.

Young Lindbergh's daring flight from New York to Paris in May of 1927 was both a culmination of all that had gone before and the beginning of a new age. The tremendous outpouring of emotion that greeted his triumph had long been nurtured by the many brave flights in previous years. Yet it can be said, too, that Lindbergh did more to arouse a popular interest in the future of aviation than any other flyer in its history. His brilliant success was of particular importance in reawakening the air enthusiasm of the American people. And in an age of cant and money-making his modesty and singleness of purpose endeared him to his millions of admirers. In France he was overwhelmed by delirious crowds, still suffering from the loss of their own aviators, Nungesser and Coli, over the Atlantic less than two weeks earlier. Their hearts went out to this "gosse" who had succeeded ; but a minority crowded around him with money-making schemes. Lindbergh's answer was typical : "This expedition wasn't organized for making money, but to advance the cause of aviation."

Despite his boyish charm, Lindbergh was a seasoned pilot. He had been a barnstormer, and an airmail pilot. Though near perfect weather favored him in his Paris flight, he left little else to chance. His *Spirit of St. Louis*, built by Claude Ryan, was right for the job, and he had the skill, steadiness and courage to push the great adventure through. He took off on a grey and drizzly morning. Thirty-three and a half hours later he flew into Le Bourget, brilliantly illuminated at night, to be received by an enormous and excited crowd. Lindbergh and aviation had become one.

Lindbergh's flight stimulated a host of new attempts. Within the year there were 31 crossings of the Atlantic. Ten were successful, but 20 people died. Thereafter, and up to the war, the flights were legion. In 1928 the Australian,

Kingsford-Smith, flew the length of the Pacific in his Fokker trimotor, *Southern Cross*. Costes and Bellonte covered the Atlantic nonstop from Paris to New York in 1930, and in 1931 and 1933 the American, Wiley Post, circled the globe. Of the many women flyers, Amelia Earhart, "Lady Lindy," the first woman to cross the Atlantic, was most beloved. She disappeared over the Pacific in 1937.

By this time the great flights had achieved their purpose. Europe was rapidly expanding its air service, and in the United States, with passage of the Kelly and Air Commerce Acts of 1925 and 1926, the necessary government stimulation for commercial aviation had at last been provided. Gradually, between 1925 and 1927, the government's airmail routes were transferred to private operators. It was not possible at first to carry more than a very few passengers along with the mail. Returning from Europe in triumph in 1927, Lindbergh said : "All Europe looks on our airmail service with reverence . . . but, whereas we have air lines, they have passenger lines." Passenger lines, however, were not long in coming.

Wall Street, impressed with the growth of the mail routes and the flying enthusiasm engendered by Lindbergh's flight, began to take a new interest in aviation. With money flowing into it, the industry began a forced growth that in a few years would carry it ahead of Europe. Financial promoters began to merge airlines with aircraft, tool, and engine companies in larger and richer aggregates. In 1928, the main transcontinental route fell into the hands of a complex of companies centering on United Airlines. Other great airlines were beginning to

68

69

70

71

emerge—T.W.A. and American Airways (later American Airlines). By 1929, when the stock market crash plunged the country into depression, the United States was already leading the world in air transportation—passengers, mail, and express. The great depression hardly checked the growth.

In 1934, in the iconoclastic atmosphere of the New Deal, the Senate uncovered favoritism in the awarding of the airmail contracts. The government promptly cancelled them all, and for a few months the mails were flown, disastrously, by inexperienced Army pilots. But the contracts, after rebidding, were soon returned to private operators. From this redistribution of the routes emerged the modern airlines of the United States.

In the 1930's, too, following the great transoceanic flights of the previous decade, the international air routes of the world were established. Since land planes could not yet be depended upon for the longer water routes, seaplanes—ever larger, ever more luxurious, ever more expensive—became the instruments of this expansion. The Lufthansa, catapulting its dependable Dornier Wal seaplanes from a ship, provided an early link with South America. In 1929, in a premature bid for the transatlantic trade, Germany launched the mammoth, 12-engined, 52-ton DO-X flying boat, which actually lumbered across to New York in 1930-31. But its engines were not powerful enough for its bulk, and its poor performance and many accidents doomed it to failure. The real pioneer flying boats of the period were the luxurious, twin-engined American ships, the Sikorsky S-38 of 1928 and the Consolidated

72

Commodore of 1929, and Britain's larger, six-engined Short flying boat of 1932.

In subsequent years the nations of Europe began to build a network of air routes around the globe. French, Belgians and British began to push into Africa, the Middle East, and the Orient. The Dutch reached the Netherlands East Indies in 1928. Air France, formed in 1933, developed services to Brazil via Africa one way, and to Indo-China the other. In the meantime a pygmy airline, formed in the United States in 1927 to serve the Caribbean, began its quick growth into the giant Pan American of later years. Pan American rapidly pushed its routes down both coasts of South America, flying over open water, jungles, and mountain ranges. The next challenge was the Atlantic and the Pacific.

Since no existing planes were capable of transoceanic service, Pan American built up its own fleet of giant flying boats. First was the Sikorsky S-40, a four-engined luxury liner with walnut-panelled walls, heavy silk draperies, and upholstered chairs. No sooner was it in service than Pan American put out specifications for an even larger plane. Only Sikorsky and Martin accepted the challenge. Sikorsky's S-42 was delivered in 1934 ; Martin's M-130,

which surpassed it in all departments, entered service in 1936, and with it Pan American inaugurated its Pacific flights from California to Manila. In its huge interior 12 to 18 pampered passengers were magnificently housed and fed.

Last of the series, the famous double-decked Boeing 314 Clipper, served on the Atlantic and Pacific runs. Atlantic service did not start until 1939, but the first test crossings were made in 1937 by a Pan American S-42 and a British Empire flying boat. The first of the huge, four-engined Empire boats, Britain's challenge to Pan American, were delivered in 1936. A fleet of 35 thereafter served in Africa and the east and with Australia's Quantas, while three of them pioneered the Atlantic run. Pan American's New Zealand service, planned by 1937, did not start until 1940. A year later, when a shuttle service opened between Australia and New Zealand, an Anglo-American round-the-world service had become a reality. But the magnificent old flying boats that had made it all possible were soon to be retired in favor of less comfortable but more efficient planes.

Also doomed were the great Zeppelins of the period, which provided the most luxurious aerial travel ever known to man. The *Graf*

73

Zeppelin first flew in 1928 and thereafter cruised around the world on scheduled and unscheduled flights. In 1936 it was moved to the South American run when the larger and more powerful *Hindenburg* began a weekly service between Lakehurst, New Jersey, and Friedrichshafen. The 72 passengers on the *Hindenburg* enjoyed oceanliner comfort with complete absence of vibration, motion, or noise. They dined sumptuously at tables set with linen and silver, slept in comfortable staterooms, and could walk freely about the ship. Accommodations included a lounge, complete with piano, a smoking room and bar, and two long promenade decks on either side of the passenger area which afforded a magnificent view of the ground not far below—for these ships flew slowly and at no great height. The dirigible era was brought to a close with the fiery end of the *Hindenburg* at Lakehurst on May 6, 1937. Comfortable as they were, dirigibles were too clumsy, too slow, too expensive, and too vulnerable for the modern age.

With the retirement of the dirigible, lighter-than-air craft had finally lost out to the airplane. Barrage balloons and blimps would prove useful during World War II, but not much beyond it. During the 1930's and thereafter free balloons were occasionally used by such explorers as Professor Auguste Piccard or Captain Albert Stevens of the U.S. Army to search the upper atmosphere. But these were highly specialized craft. The modern helicopter, which today has certainly achieved the status of a short-range transport, was initially developed during the 1920's and 1930's, while Juan de la Cierva's Autogiro made an outstanding flight from London into France in 1928. But rotarywinged planes remained experimental until after World War II.

It was the multi-engined, heavy land transport that in the end elbowed out every other form of air transportation, whether over land or sea. The rapidly growing airlines required a transport capable of carrying a large number of passengers from one place to another at maximum speed but at minimum expense. Obviously, neither the luxury flying boats nor the dirigibles met these requirements ; nor, for a long time, did the various types of land transports in use around the world. The United States, coming up from behind as usual, finally put together many elements, largely developed in Europe, to produce the first of the modern transports, the DC-3 of 1935, which "did more for

74

75

75 The "Graf Zeppelin" enters her hangar at Friedrichshafen. She first flew in 1928, made a 22-day trip around the world in 1929, was then put on Atlantic run.
76 The "Graf Zeppelin" was 776 ft. long, loaded, weighed 258,000 lbs., required a large crew to land her.
77 The "Graf Zeppelin" landing. In 1936 the "Hindenburg," carrying 72 passengers to her 20, replaced her on the North Atlantic run. The burning of the "Hindenburg" in 1937 closed the dirigible era.

the advancement of commercial aviation than any single plane ever built." Safe, dependable, cheap to operate, the DC-3, could carry 21 passengers at 180 miles per hour. It cut flying time in half on the transcontinental route, and by 1939 it was in use on almost every airline in the world.

It was an all-metal, thick-winged, internally braced monoplane with a thin fuselage, and it was heavy enough to carry two of the new, more powerful, radial aircooled engines, their drag reduced by a streamlined cowling. Many of its features had appeared in the earlier German planes, especially the remarkable, low-wing Junkers F-13 monoplane of 1919, and on the famous trimotors, the Fokker, and the Ford (the "old tin goose"), both of 1925. Its immediate predecessors in the United States were the fast Lockheed Vegas and Air Expresses of 1927 and 1928, and the all-metal, Boeing-247 of 1933. It was Donald Douglas's genius to combine all the necessary elements, many of them known but disregarded for many years, in a plane that has seldom been equalled for overall efficiency.

With the DC-3 and its successors, America's dominance on the commercial air routes of the world was a foregone conclusion. In Europe, at the time of the DC-3, there were 79 types of transports, operated by 50-odd companies. And many of these were giant, awkward biplanes like the British Hercules, Argosy, and Handley-Page, or the French Breguets and Farmans. They were comfortable, they were magnificent, but they belonged to an earlier age. The future of commercial aviation lay with the American heavy transport.

76

78 Hitler's Luftwaffe flies by at Nuremberg in 1938.
Built up secretly, it was unveiled in 1935, leading
to British, and eventually American air
rearmament.

Describing the war of the future, General Giulio Douhet of the Italian Air Force wrote in 1921 : "No longer can areas exist in which life can be lived in safety and tranquillity, nor can the battlefield any longer be limited to actual combatants. . . . There will be no distinction any longer between soldiers and civilians." This frightening view, based upon the General's conviction that the next war would be fought in the air, did little to make him popular with a public grown weary of war. Nor did the soldiers like his idea of an air arm completely independent of the other services. Both shuddered at the picture he drew of a mighty bombing force, carrying the attack deep into enemy territory to destroy both its cities and its industrial centers. Here and there a few other prophets of the future shared Douhet's views as well as his unpopularity. There was General William E. Mitchell, the father of American military aviation, and Air Marshal Sir Hugh Trenchard, for ten years Britain's Chief of Air Staff. These men were indeed prophets ; but they had little honor in their day.

The people wanted to forget war. Lloyd George had often called the recent bloody conflict "the war to end war." And now it was ended. With Germany disarmed and Russia still prostrated by its revolution, the victorious Allies, with almost unseemly haste, dismantled their huge war machines and turned to thoughts of disarmament. Budgets, especially for aircraft, were cut to the bone, the costly heavy bomber suffering most of all. New designs were cancelled (huge existing stocks of surplus wartime planes and engines, moreover, would discourage new designing well into the 1930's) and military

79 *General William E. Mitchell.*

establishments were reduced to a hard core of older—and generally conservative—career men. In England Sir Hugh Trenchard, under persistent attack, just managed to maintain the independence of the Royal Air Force. Italy's Regia Aeronautica, after a period of eclipse, became an independent service in 1923 and under such leaders as General Italo Balbo showed a good deal of spirit ; but the Italian Air Force would continue to be tied far too closely to the support of ground and naval forces. Alone, the French Air Force appeared to be relatively strong and well equipped ; but this would prove to be a delusion.

The career of General "Billy" Mitchell best illustrates the temper of the times. Assistant Chief of the Army Air Service from 1919 to 1925, Mitchell devoted an aggressive and colorful personality to a national crusade for the recognition of airpower. Fiercely joining issue with the conservatives both within and outside the armed forces, he advocated an independent air arm and a wider acceptance of the warplane, especially the heavy bomber, as a weapon of attack. He encouraged commercial aviation, and staged Air Service flights across the country and even around the world to dramatize aviation's potential. To prove the vulnerability of the battleship to air attack, his bombers sank three German warships in 1921, a feat that aroused much interest abroad, especially in England. Most of Mitchell's predictions were to come true, but he had fatally antagonized powerful elements in the armed forces, and in 1926 he was court-martialed for insubordination, found guilty, and suspended from the army for five years. He resigned before the sentence could take effect.

Mitchell's younger disciples within the Air Service continued to agitate for a long-range bomber striking force, but little could be accomplished. The Navy, although resentful of Mitchell's attacks on its battleships, saw eye to eye with him on the need for naval air forces. While experimenting with planes launched from submarines or catapulted from cruisers, the Navy took its cue from Britain and commissioned its first modern carrier, the converted collier *Langley*, in 1922. By 1927 two battle cruisers had been converted into the 35,000-ton carriers *Lexington* and *Saratoga* of World War II fame. These were matched by the Royal Navy's new *Eagle* and *Hermes*. Both navies, too, built up fleets of giant dirigibles, but a series of accidents and fatal crashes spelled the end for these beautiful ships. Of the United States Navy's four dirigibles, all but the *Los Angeles* met disaster.

Flying boats, however, were just coming into their own. In 1933, for instance, Italo Balbo led 24 twin-engined boats from Italy via Canada to the World's Fair at Chicago. In the next year six American P2Y's, predecessors of the famed wartime PBY, flew all the way from San Francisco to Hawaii. Generally, though, progress in military aviation was slow, and well into the 1930's the air fleets of most nations were dominated by huge, lumbering bombers and stubby little biplane fighters, not too different from their wartime predecessors. The high-speed fighter designs of the future had their origin in the international Schneider Cup seaplane races, which in the 1920's began to develop sleek, very fast monoplanes with clean lines. England's famed wartime Spitfire, for instance, grew out

80 *French prewar fighter, Bloch-151.*

81 Stubby, slow Boeing P-12
fighters, typical military
planes of interwar period.

of one of these designs. America's Army Pulitzer races also contributed to the advance of fighter design.

Persistent agitation for heavy bombers, both in Britain and in the United States, had been matched by equally persistent opposition. In the early 1930's, while England was making small headway, Mitchell's American disciples were finally able to create a small force of true long-range, strategic bombers, designed along the lines of the heavy transport of the day. First came the fast, all-metal Martin B-10; then the famous four-engined B-17 Flying Fortress, with a 2,000-mile range, two of which were hesitently accepted by the Air Corps in 1936. Its companion heavy bomber, the B-24 Liberator, was rushed into production in 1939.

Germany, denied a military establishment by the Treaty of Versailles, grew restive after the war when the Allies made little progress toward disarmament, and in many ingenious ways began to build up a clandestine air establishment. Aircraft companies set up branches abroad while at home the civil air line, Lufthansa, kept the industry alive. Young Germans were encouraged to take up gliding, while others acquired valuable pilot experience training the Russian Air Force. After a series of excellent modern prototypes were created, Germany secretly began to plan a new air force. At Nuremberg in 1935 Hitler, with dramatic suddenness, unveiled the new Luftwaffe before a frightened world. Germany had become a major power in the air.

The period of the 1930's, haunted by the memory of World War I, displays a curious ambivalence. While Germany was rearming in the name of a New Order designed to redress its wartime grievances, the Allies, still recoiling from the horrors of the war, were striving desperately to create a world without arms. The League of Nations Disarmament Conference, meeting in 1932, made a final, earnest effort to achieve agreement while the Allied nations, awaiting the outcome, let their defenses deteriorate. Meanwhile, the world began once more to slide toward war. Japan invaded China, Hitler began to create his new Germany, Italy snatched at Ethiopia, Spain (where Hitler tried out his new warplanes) erupted into civil war, and the League of Nations, after Germany, Italy, and Japan had resigned, began to disintegrate. The Disarmament Conference itself came to a weary, fruitless end in 1934.

Visiting Germany in 1936, Charles Lindbergh was impressed by the power of the German Air Force, but his words of warning were hardly listened to when he returned to America. In the same year two British Ministers, John Simon and Anthony Eden, returned from Germany to report that the Luftwaffe had already reached parity with the Royal Air Force and planned soon to surpass the French. The French Air Force, still the largest, had about 2,000 firstline craft, but it was capable only of close ground support, and was hopelessly decentralized. Its industrial base was weak, and its planes mostly obsolete. The British, on the contrary, alarmed by the German threat, reorganized the Royal Air Force, planned a rapid expansion, ordered a force of new, four-engined bombers and secretly began to organize a radar defense network. Britain's continued weakness on land and in the

82 American aircraft
production line in California.
During the war U.S. firms,
building some 300,000 planes
for American and Allied air
forces, helped turn the tide.
83 British Spitfire in flight.
This famous fighter also helped
to turn the tide—against the
Luftwaffe, preparing for the
German invasion in 1940.

82

air—as well as that of France—largely dictated the capitulation to Hitler at the time of the Munich Agreement in 1938 ; but thereafter the Royal Air Force began to grow at a rapid pace.

Although the United States at this time possessed a few heavy bombers, the concept of strategic bombing was still under attack as being both barbarous and unnecessary. But the Munich crisis did its work, and when General H. H. Arnold, a Mitchell disciple, was appointed Chief of the Air Corps the future of the bomber program was assured. In far-off Japan the Navy for many years had quietly been building up a formidable fleet, with special emphasis on carriers and swift fighter craft. The Russians, following the ideas of Douhet after World War I, had specialized for a time in huge, four-engined bombers ; but after the importance of attack-aviation had been demonstrated in the Spanish War, they began to emphasize close cooperation with the army command. The massing of parachute troops was a Russian idea, although used for the most part by other nations during the war.

The stage was set for World War II. With frightening suddenness Germany attacked Poland on September 1, 1939, and a shocked world was quickly made to realize the new importance of airpower. Pacing the armored divisions, 2,000 planes destroyed the Polish Air Force on its fields, bombed Warsaw and lesser centers, and strafed and dive-bombed hordes of disorganized soldiers and civilians on the roads. Russia then moved in from the east, and it was all over in a month. In April 1940, after an interval of calm, the Germans overran Denmark

and Norway, flying in a company of paratroops and thousands of soldiers to supplement those debarked from ships. British amphibious landings in the face of German air superiority were easily repulsed, teaching the proud Royal Navy a bitter lesson in the paramount need for air cover.

But all of this was merely a rehearsal for what was to come. Attacking Holland, Belgium, and France in May, the Germans unleashed in its full power their "blitzkrieg," characterized by the close coordination of aerial units with fast-moving armored columns in a furious, concentrated assault. Some 1,600 aircraft bombed Rotterdam savagely, and dropped airborne troops on airfields and other vital points, while Stuka divebombers terrorized military columns and fleeing refugees. Holland was quickly defeated, Belgium fell soon afterwards. The British army, leaving behind its equipment, managed to escape by sea at Dunkirk. France held on for a while, but capitulated in June after Italy had entered the war on the side of Germany.

In this classic blitzkrieg the Allied air forces fought desperately, but were outnumbered and outmaneuvered by the enemy. The Luftwaffe appeared cruelly invincible ; but its grave weaknesses would soon be revealed. Planned for a short, savage attack, it had few spare parts and planes available. Its bombers, though fast and well-designed, were light and inadequately armed. Above all, it was designed and trained primarily for close support of land operations. And now the land fighting was over and the enemy lay far across the Channel. Although about 3,000 German planes, based on some

83

300 fields, faced a scant 700 craft in England, the Royal Air Force had become a truly independent, offensive unit with excellent leadership, superb planes, and skillful and daring pilots. In the Battle of Britain it was able to destroy some 1,733 German planes to under 1,000 lost of its own ; and it averted both invasion and defeat. Churchill's words had a special meaning : "Never in the field of human conflict was so much owed by so many to so few."

The battle began in August, first with coastal strikes, then with attacks on airfields and aircraft factories. When these began to tell, a daring British raid on Berlin diverted the bombers in retaliation to London and other cities. The climax of the battle came in mid-September, when the Luftwaffe was severely defeated and the German-held Channel ports were so ceaselessly pounded that the projected German invasion had to be postponed. The massive "blitz" bombing of London and other cities followed—which proved little but the extreme vulnerability of the German bombers. Attacks continued well into the next year—but the Battle of Britain had long ago been lost.

The Luftwaffe again showed its superiority in its chosen field in the conquests of Yugoslavia, Greece, and Crete. Crete was overwhelmed in May of 1941 in a massive airborne assault, superbly staged, which, as in Norway, caught the British without adequate air cover. And in the ill-fated invasion of Russia in June the Luftwaffe again spearheaded the attack with some 3,500 planes, easily driving back the Russian Air Force, which was more than twice as large but inferior in quality—having suffered a drastic reorganization in 1939 after the Spanish

and Finnish wars had revealed its weaknesses. Enough was left after the initial German blitzkrieg, however, for it to play an important part in turning back the Germans from Moscow. This was the beginning of the end.

The dreadful Russian winter then set in. Spread thinly over a front 1,875 miles long, the Luftwaffe could do no more than hold its own, while transports from Poland were called in to supply encircled German troops. At Stalingrad during the next winter the growing Russian Air Force, reinforced by planes from the Allies, gained air supremacy at last. By the end of the battle only 2,000 German planes on the whole front were left to oppose over 10,000 Russian ones. During the next two years the Luftwaffe, increasingly on the defensive, took its part in the hopeless, weary retreat of the German forces, desperately fighting off a vastly superior enemy air fleet which was now being reinforced at the rate of 3,000 planes a month. Among the most savage air battles of the entire war were those fought between the Russians and the Germans over doomed Berlin.

"The fighters are our salvation," Churchill wrote in 1940, near the climax of the Battle of Britain, "but the bombers alone provide the means of victory." No Allied invasion of Europe could be mounted until air supremacy had been won ; but it was impossible to start the air offensive until the dangerous submarine threat to Britain's lifelines across the Atlantic had been overcome. During 1941 Britain's few bombers had to be thrown into the struggle, and when the United States became increasingly involved and finally entered the war that year, blimps, seaplanes, baby carriers, American

84 *American B-24's drop incendiaries over Kiel, Germany in 1943 while B-17's higher up (not shown) bomb the submarine yards. The British night-bombing attacks reached a climax in 1943 with a fire-raid on Hamburg. But the American day bombers, suffering heavy losses from German fighters, had to be provided with escorts for protection.*
85 *B-24 gunner waits for German attack.*

85

bombers, and anything else that would serve went out over the Atlantic from east and west to do battle with the German submarines. Victory in the Battle of the Atlantic was not assured until late in 1943 ; but even while it was being fought the transport commands of the British and the Americans had been building up long-range air routes (flown by transport versions of the heavy bombers) to ferry personnel, supplies, and new planes across the Atlantic. These busy routes were eventually extended around the world and formed the model for the far-flung intercontinental air lanes of the post-war period.

By the opening of 1942 it began to be possible to plan the mighty Anglo-American air offensive over Europe. And by this time, too, American war production had begun to turn out thousands of weapons on a mass assembly basis. Some 300,000 airplanes alone were to be built in the United States by the end of the war. Early in 1942 the American Eighth Air Force had been established in Britain, and the British heavy bombers—the Stirling, the Lancaster, and the Halifax—had begun to come into service. The American B-17's and B-24's were designed for daylight bombing with the accurate Norden bombsight, but the British had already been committed to night "area" bombing of industrial targets. The British offensive began first, and in earnest, with a 1,000-bomber raid on Cologne in May and reached a climax with the incredible "fire" raid on Hamburg in July and August of 1943. After a tentative start in 1942 the American bombers concentrated during 1943 on the German aircraft and allied industries, but after initial successes began to run into serious trouble

as the Germans responded with an accelerated production of fighters. Bomber losses began to mount dangerously. Over the ball-bearing works at Schweinfurt, for instance, 16 per cent of the bombers were destroyed and many more damaged. The American missions had to be cut down until the new P-51 Mustang could be provided as a long-range fighter escort.

Early in 1944 a reinforced Eighth Air Force resumed the attack, with full fighter protection, and by mid-spring had won its battle against the enemy interceptors. Having lost over 800 fighters in February and March, the Germans were beginning to run short of trained and experienced pilots. The B-17's could now range freely over Germany. In March 1,000 Fortresses dropped their bombs over Berlin, already crippled by repeated British attacks. With the Luftwaffe on the defensive, the conditions were at last established for the long-expected invasion of the continent, which took place on June 6, after Allied bombers had unremittingly pounded the German positions across the Channel. Some 11,000 aircraft of all types participated in the massive assault, and as the Allied troops pushed through France and into Germany, they continued to disrupt the communications of the enemy far behind the lines.

Indeed, from the first offensive in Egypt in 1942 to the final battles inside Germany, the Allied armies, building upon the idea of the German blitzkrieg, had relied heavily upon airpower, both tactical and strategic. Bombers and fighters had paced the offensive from Egypt into Tunisia. Air cover had protected the Anglo-American landings in North Africa, and heavy

86

bombers had softened up Italy for the final surrender in 1943. As early as 1942 American B-24's had bombed the Ploesti oil fields from African bases. Later, heavy bombers of the American Air Forces, based in Tunisia and then at Foggia in Italy, had continuously attacked targets in Austria, Germany, and France in cooperation with the bombers based in Britain. Airpower in every form had indeed made an indispensable contribution to the successful assault upon "Fortress Europe."

The Pacific war began, too, with a masterly use of airpower—the Japanese assault upon Pearl Harbor on December 7, 1941, by carrier-based planes, which practically wiped out American air and sea power in the Pacific. Later the Japanese attacked the British in Malaya, sank their only two battleships, and by February 1942 had seized Singapore. By June the swollen Japanese empire stretched from the Aleutians to India and lapped at Australia to the south. The Japanese air forces had shown their strength (the famous Zero fighter had proved outstanding) but it soon became evident that they were limited, even more than the Luftwaffe, to close support of army and navy actions.

Although General James H. Doolittle led a daring raid over Japan with 16 light bombers in April 1942, the Allied counteroffensive really began after the naval battles of the Coral Sea and Midway in May and June—marked by the first long-range air battles between carrier forces—which once and for all stopped the Japanese expansion. Gaining a foothold in the Solomons, the Allied forces began to fight painfully westward, gradually wearing down the enemy's air and naval strength while their own was increasingly reinforced by mounting war production at home. Soon troops under General Douglas MacArthur began to move along New Guinea toward the Philippines and Japan, while in a parallel campaign to the north a huge naval task force under Admiral Chester Nimitz, built around carriers, "hopped" from island to island, softening up each one with carrier strikes and bomber raids in preparation for the amphibious assault. The attack upon the Marianas precipitated the Battle of the Philippine Sea which dealt a heavy blow to the carrier forces of the enemy. A few months later American B-29 Superfortresses were flying off the Marianas against Japan.

They had been flying somewhat earlier from China, but the difficulty of supplying them, and the other American forces, over the "Hump" of the Himalayas vitiated the effort. Later, in a jungle campaign supported largely from the air, Burma was reconquered, reopening the "Burma Road" to China. As new bases came into operation the B-29 offensive, designed to prepare the Japanese islands for a projected invasion, grew heavier. Despite swarms of "kamikaze" suicide planes, Iwo Jima and Okinawa were captured in some of the bloodiest battles of the war. Then from May through July of 1945 the matchstick cities of Japan literally exploded into flames under a rain of firebombs from thousands of low-flying B-29's. Japan was already close to defeat when on August 6 Hiroshima was devastated by a single atom bomb. On August 9, Nagasaki suffered the same fate. Japan surrendered, and without the planned invasion. Airpower had made it unnecessary.

87 

JAPAN AT WAR WITH U.S.
Hawaii, Philippines
Bombed; 104 Killed
CONGRESS TO ACT

*89 Modern jet airliners nestle close to the latest
in air terminals at San Francisco. Adjustable
walkways protect passengers and allow them to enter
planes at cabin level.*

Aviation's period of trial was over. It had emerged from World War II full-grown, an accepted fact of life. But as the years went by its triumph would prove to be only another beginning ; for as the airplane was swept up in the technological revolution of the postwar era it underwent, in scarcely more than a decade, more changes in design, power, and function than in all the years since it had first left the ground.

Right after the war, it is true, there was a period of faltering while the giant aircraft industry, suddenly deprived of its war orders, was forced to negotiate the difficult transition to a peacetime economy. Some companies began nervously to diversify into consumer areas ill-suited to their capabilities while others tried again, with little success, to sell light planes to the man in the street. It began to look uncomfortably like the aftermath of World War I. But this time it was to be a different story. After World War II the importance of military aviation could no longer be doubted, though its precise role in warfare might still be questioned. Warplanes of every type had been in action in every theater of the war. They had flown over every ocean and had penetrated the remotest jungles and snowbound wildernesses of the world, leaving behind them serviceable airports wherever they had operated. Above all the heavy transport, which did not exist during and after World War I, had proved itself a dependable carrier on land and over the sea.

Commercial aviation in the postwar era was completely dominated by the United States. The American heavy transport had been per-

90 *The world's first pure jet airliner, the British De Havilland Comet, went into service in 1952, now flies, in an improved version, for B.E.A., B.O.A.C., and other airlines. The Russian twin-jet Tu-104 entered service in 1957, the big American Boeing 707's in 1958, and the French twin-jet Caravelle in 1959. These transports offer speed; but not enough. In a few years supersonic liners, flying twice as fast, will circle the world in half the time.*

Douglas Super DC-3
U.S.A.
Twin-engined airliner
Wingspan: 90 ft.
Length: 67 ft. 8½ in.
Cruising speed: 251 m.p.h
Range: 1425 miles
Passengers: 30-38

Boeing 377 Stratocruiser
U.S.A.
Four-engined airliner
Wingspan: 141 ft. 3 in.
Length: 110 ft. 4 in.
Cruising speed: 340 m.p.h.
Range: 4600 miles
Passengers: 55-100

Douglas DC-4
U.S.A.
Four-engined airliner
Wingspan: 117 ft. 6 in.
Length: 93 ft. 11 in.
Cruising speed: 239 m.p.h.
Range: 1500 miles
Passengers: 22-44

Convair 440 Metropolitan
U.S.A.
Twin-engined medium-range
airliner
Wingspan: 105 ft. 4 in.
Length: 79 ft. 2 in.
Cruising speed: 289 m.p.h.
Range: 1040 miles
Passengers: 44-52

Curtiss Commando
U.S.A.
Twin-engined transport
Wingspan: 108 ft.
Length: 76 ft. 6 in.
Cruising speed: 277 m.p.h.
Range: 1857 miles
Used mainly as troop
transport

Martin 404
U.S.A.
Twin-engined medium-range
airliner
Wingspan: 93 ft. 3 in.
Length: 74 ft. 7 in.
Cruising speed: 280 m.p.h.
Range: 805 miles
Passengers: 40

Lockheed Constellation —
Model 749A
U.S.A.
Four-engined long-range airliner
Wingspan: 123 ft.
Length: 95 ft. 1¼ in.
Cruising speed: 328 m.p.h.
Range: 3000 miles
Passengers: 44-64

Douglas DC-6
U.S.A.
Four-engined airliner
Wingspan: 117 ft. 6 in.
Length: 100 ft. 7 in.
Cruising speed: 313 m.p.h.
Range: 3820 miles
Passengers: 48-58

Lockheed 1649A Starliner
U.S.A.
Four-engined long-range
airliner
Wingspan: 150 ft.
Length: 116 ft. 2 in.
Cruising speed: 342 m.p.h.
Range: 7200 miles
Passengers: 58-92

Douglas DC-7C Seven Seas
U.S.A.
Four-engined
intercontinental airliner
Wingspan: 127 ft. 6 in.
Length: 112 ft. 3 in.
Cruising speed: 346 m.p.h.
Range: 4635 miles
Passengers: 62-99

91 (next page.) Pilot's cockpit on a Convair 880 jet airliner, one of a series which includes the larger 600 and 990. Convairs are the latest entry in the American field of jet transports.
92 (next page) View of the Alps from a Swissair DC-8, flying between Zurich and Geneva. The jet DC-8 is the latest of the famous Douglas liners.

De Havilland Comet 4
Great Britain
Four-engined jet airliner
Wingspan: 114 ft. 10 in.
Length: 111 ft. 6 in.
Cruising speed: 500 m.p.h.
Range: 2820 miles
Passengers: 60-81

Fokker F.27 Friendship
Holland
Twin turboprop-engined
airliner
Wingspan: 95 ft. 2 in.
Length: 77 ft. 2 in.
Cruising speed: 275 m.p.h.
Range: 1620 miles
Passengers: 32-40

Vickers Viscount
Great Britain
Four-engined airliner
Wingspan: 93 ft. 8½ in.
Length: 81 ft. 9 in.
Cruising speed: 324 m.p.h.
Range: 1035 miles
Passengers: 40-59

Tu-114 "Cleat"
Russia
Four-engined airliner
Wingspan: 177 ft. 2 in.
Length: 154 ft. 10 in.
Cruising speed: 565 m.p.h.
Range: 6214 miles
Passengers: 120-220

Tu-104 "Camel"
Russia
Twin-jet airliner
Wingspan: 114 ft. 10 in.
Length: 121 ft. 5 in.
Cruising speed: 515 m.p.h.
Range: 2000 miles
Passengers: 50

Douglas DC-8
U.S.A.
Four-engined jet airliner
Wingspan: 139 ft. 9 in.
Length: 150 ft. 6 in.
Cruising speed: 589 m.p.h.
Range: 5725 miles
Passengers: 118-176

Bristol Britannia
Great Britain
Four-engined airliner
Wingspan: 142 ft. 3½ in.
Length: 114 ft.
Cruising speed: 361 m.p.h.
Range: 3450 miles
Passengers: 73-133

Sud-Aviation S.E. 210
Caravelle
France
Twin-jet medium-range airliner
Wingspan: 112 ft. 6 in.
Length: 104 ft. 10 in.
Cruising speed: 515 m.p.h.
Range: 1500 miles
Passengers: 64-80

Boeing 707-320
Intercontinental
U.S.A.
Four-engined jet airliner
Wingspan: 142 ft. 5 in.
Length: 152 ft. 11 in.
Cruising speed: 605 m.p.h.
Range: 4730 miles
Passengers: 110-162

Convair 880
U.S.A.
Four-jet medium-range
airliner
Wingspan: 120 ft.
Length: 129 ft. 4 in.
Cruising speed: 583 m.p.h.
Range: 3000 miles
Passengers: 88-109

fected in the late 1930's, just in time for the war, and by agreement with the British the United States had furnished most of the wartime transports for the Allies. Thus thousands of its carriers were available at the end of the war to satisfy the pent-up demand for passenger and air freight transports. Four-engined DC-4's, which in the late years of the war had been flying the Atlantic at the rate of one each hour, represented almost half of the world's war-surplus transports. The indestructible DC-3, the Boeing 307, and the Constellation had also seen war service, and in the first years of peace were eagerly gobbled up by the stricken airlines of the world. K.L.M., as an example, having lost most of its facilities, began the postwar era with just three war-surplus DC-3's.

It was not merely a matter of availability. The American manufacturers, with years of experience in the mass-production of low-cost, high-efficiency transports, had learned to build the best planes in the world ; and well into the 1950's they continued to dominate the market with their piston carriers. Douglas, which had produced 11,000 twin-engined DC's by 1945, went on improving its series right through the DC-6 and DC-7. The graceful Lockheed Constellation, and the Super Constellation of 1952 ; the double-decked Boeing Stratocruiser (developed from the B-29 bomber) ; the medium-range, twin-engined Convair and other planes flew for the airlines of many nations. The larger craft, moreover, were used on all the longer sea-routes, since the increased range, dependability, and economy of the land transport had put the flying boat out of business as an intercontinental carrier.

Geography, too, played its part. Within the vast, unified land-mass of the United States, unimpeded by the national frontiers, customs barriers, and conflicting aims of Europe, civil aviation soon began to show enormous progress and in time began to stimulate the aviation of other nations. In 1958, the airlines of the United States flew 39.5 million people on domestic routes, while another 4.2 million were carried on their international and overseas routes. During the same year more people crossed the Atlantic from the United States by air than by steamship, surely a turning point in the history of transportation.

Outside the United States, curiously enough, civil aviation has had its fastest growth and its greatest impact in underdeveloped areas such as Latin America and Africa, where natural resources are abundant and land communications poor. In Brazil, a vast land covered with jungles and swamps, air transportation has been practically remaking the country. Air freight, too, which in the postwar years grew even faster than passenger-carrying, has been of inestimable importance, not only in settled areas such as the United States, but also in less-developed countries. In Australia, for instance, it was discovered that the long-range transport of meat was far more economical by air than by rail.

Low-fare tourist flights, pioneered by some American lines in 1949 and spurred on thereafter by stiff competition from non-scheduled, low-margin air carriers, helped mightily to stimulate the growth of air travel. Ultimately even the transatlantic carriers adopted the crowded tourist flight. Thanks to such devices, international air travel soon became a commonplace.

93　An impressionistic view of
San Francisco's International
Airport at night. Airports
started 50 years ago as muddy
cow pastures with a few sheds.
Today the largest airports
handle an immense traffic, and
can hardly keep abreast of the
problems posed by ever faster
planes and more and more
passengers. In the U.S. today
airliners take off or land,
around the clock, at a
staggering rate of one every
few seconds.

94 *French twin-jet Caravelle, superbly designed by Sud-Aviation, features engines at rear of the fuselage, thus reducing cabin noise to a pleasant minimum. European short and medium range planes, such as the Caravelle, and the British and Dutch turboprops, the Viscount and Fokker Friendship, have been sold in many countries, leaving the long-range market to the Americans.*

More and more of the longer flights were routed over "the top of the world," after a Scandinavian DC-6, flying from Los Angeles to Copenhagen via Greenland, had pioneered the first "great-circle" flight in 1954.

The airplane was called back into military service in 1950 when the bitter and protracted Korean War broke out. Two years earlier the Berlin Airlift, one of the most dramatic incidents of the early Cold War, had not only frustrated the Soviet designs upon the city but had demonstrated before the world the power and importance of organized air transportation. Between June of 1948 and September of 1949, American transports and British bombers flew 2,324,000 tons of essential supplies into the blockaded city, thus averting a major crisis. In 1949 came the startling disclosure that the Russians also had the atom bomb, and a year later, when the Russian-equipped army of North Korea attacked its neighbor to the south, the Cold War began to turn perilously hot.

"We lost a battle in Korea," said the American General Hoyt Vandenberg, "but airpower kept us from losing a war." In many ways the Korean War was a later and smaller World War II, fought with the same military tactics and many of the same weapons—including, in the air, the tested B-29 and B-26 bombers, the P-51 Mustang, the Corsair operating from carriers, and assorted military transports. But there were differences, too. The helicopter came into its own, showing great versatility as a light transport, observation, and ambulance plane. The Korean War, however, lives in the popular imagination for the first extensive use of jet

95   Cockpit of a Boeing 707 jet liner in flight, a scene seldom witnessed by the passengers behind the cockpit partition. Flight crew members—pilot, co-pilot, flight engineer—are carefully chosen for mental alertness, judgement, emotional stability, self control and mechanical aptitude. Pilots must have at least 200 hours of solo flying time. Flight crew members are backed up by a larger array of equally well qualified flight attendants and ground personnel.

96 *Night scene in a Boeing 707 airliner. Stewardess, who attends to passengers' needs, is usually a college graduate, is picked for poise, intelligence, and resourcefulness, is equally skilled in handling emergencies or in serving meals. Because of speed of jet liners, passengers may cover 625 miles while eating dinner — 300 miles given to the main course, 150 miles to the dessert.*

fighters in combat. When the Chinese intervened late in 1950 with their versatile Russian Mig-15's, American Sabre Jet F-86's were thrown in to meet the challenge and soon established their over-all superiority with a seven-to-one ratio of kills. Other jets took part in the war—the American F-80 Shooting Star and several carrier-borne Navy fighters, as well as the British Meteor jets of the Australian air force. The jet battles in "Mig Alley" in Korea served notice on the world that aviation, endowed with a new propulsive force, was about to take an unprecedented leap forward.

Long before World War II certain far-sighted designers, realizing that the propeller-driven plane had almost reached the upper limits of its speed potential, began to study the possibilities of the jet engine. Frank Whittle in England took out his first patents in 1930, Hans von Ohain in Germany in 1935 ; but Germany managed to get a successful turbojet aircraft, the He-178, built by Heinkel around an Ohain engine, into the air first, on August 27, 1939. England's pioneer jet, the Gloster E28/39, powered by a Whittle engine, flew almost two years later and eventually became the twin-jet Meteor, the only Allied jet plane to see service during the war.

The Meteors took part in the Normandy invasion and went into action against the "flying bombs"—jet against jet, prophetic of the future. The Germans, with their backs to the wall, had a much greater need for "wonder weapons" than the Allies and took the jet much further. Their V-1 flying bomb, a pilotless, pulse-jet bomber, terrorized London for 83 days in 1944. A number of other jet and rocket experimental interceptors were thrown up against the relentless Allied bombing attacks in the closing months of the war. The twin-jet Me-262, the world's first jet production model, of which 1,294 were built, easily outclimbed and outfought its propeller-driven opponents ; but it came too late. Harried as they were, the Germans even produced the prototype of a four-jet bomber, the Ju-287.

And so the jet had arrived. The Americans, after studying a Whittle engine, flew their first experimental jet, the Bell XP-59A, in 1942 and began to produce operational jets by the end of the war. The turbojet engine had liberated the airplane from the confines of propeller and piston ; when a British jet first flew faster than the speed of sound in 1948, the jet age was ready to be born.

The consequences of the simple substitution of jet for piston engines were enormous. Speeds were sharply increased, designs altered, military strategy upset, and the aircraft industry forced into drastic changes. Although new problems arose—in financing, air traffic control, navigation, landing facilities, manufacturing and the development of new materials—a new dimension of comfortable and rapid flight was opened for the air traveller. The coming of the jet marked a revolution in transportation comparable to the transition from sail to steam.

Since the American piston transport dominated the commercial field after the war, the British, already leading in jet engines, decided to leapfrog into the future with a bold program for high-speed jet transports. They had to pay for the honor of putting the world's first pure jet transport into service in 1952, for the De

98 Traffic at airport is
monitored by a controller with
radar scopes, the one at left for
long-range surveillance, the
one at right for close, runway
approaches. While watching
screens controller "talks in"
pilot over radio, giving
detailed instructions.
99 In bad weather pilot must
depend upon radio instructions
and beams for guidance in
landing. Once "below the
weather" he is helped in by
ground approach lights and
signals (shown at Orly, outside
Paris.)

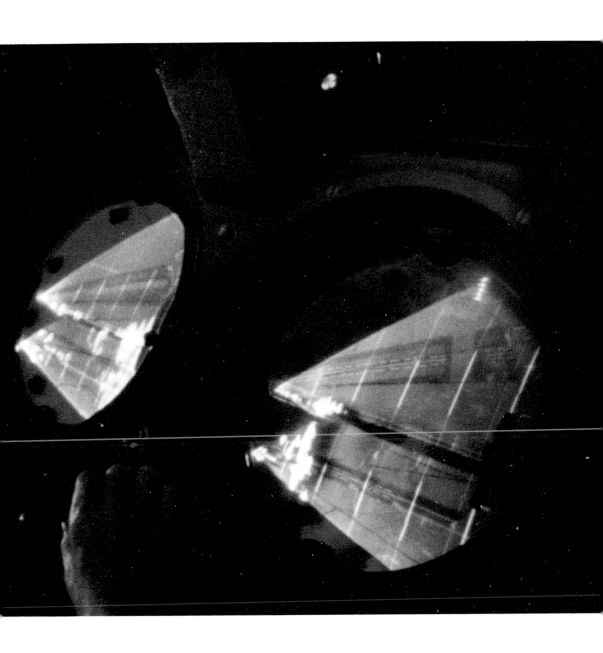

Havilland Comet, after a series of accidents, had to be withdrawn in 1954 until a safer version could be worked out.

They did far better with the first turboprop transport, the Vickers Viscount, in service by 1953, and with the much larger, long-range Bristol Britannia turboprop (1957). The speed and economy of both soon made them a favorite with many airlines.

The next entry in the jet transport race appeared suddenly at London in 1956 from far-off Russia, astonishing the Western world. It was the twin-jet Tu-104, which went into general service the following year. At the end of the war, the Russians had imported German technicians, as well as research data and actual jet engines and aircraft, and in 1947 they purchased a number of British turbo jet engines for study. The first result was the Mig-15, unveiled in Korea. Then came the Tu-104, equally unexpected. In subsequent years the prestige of Russia in the jet field was solidly established with an array of jet and turboprop bombers and transports, including the giant turboprop Tu-114, largest commercial plane in the world. Powered by four huge engines, each turning two four-bladed, counterrotating propellers, the Tu-114 can carry from 170 to 225 passengers. In 1959 it flew from Moscow to New York in a little over 11 hours.

The United States, with its heavy investment in piston transports, laid its plans for the jet age but held out to the last hour. Where speed was not a consideration, its compound piston engines—some with 28 cylinders developing 3,500 horsepower—were still the most economical in the world. But when the change came, it was rapid. In October 1958, Pan American launched the first commercial jet service to Europe with a four-engined, Boeing 707. A little over a year later 85 Boeings were in service around the world and had already carried 2,400,000 passengers! The DC-8 followed shortly, and then the Convair 880. The United States had maintained its lead in the long-range transport field, but was to be increasingly challenged by European manufacturers in the shorter ranges. The British Viscount, the Dutch Fokker F-27, and especially the sleek, twin-jet French Caravelle of 1959, a miracle of engineering, have invaded the American market itself. As a result of this healthy competition, jet transports are now giving the world the best and most extensive air transportation it has ever known.

Private and business (or "general") aviation, has also grown by leaps and bounds. In the United States in 1958 planes of this type outnumbered the airline fleet by 40 to one. Indeed, the range and variety of modern civil aviation is astonishing. Imagine, for instance, a jetliner coming in over the shores of a hypothetical continent. Far below it small planes hover, spotting fish for the fishing boats. Inland, as it approaches the big city, many more small craft are visible. A "flying farmer" is dusting his crops against blight, a builder is surveying a housing development from the air, sportsmen are cruising around for the fun of it. Higher up a heavy air freight transport speeds fresh fish, perishable fruit, or live chicks to distant markets, two-engined business planes hurry executives to lunch-time appointments, while several shorthaul transports take off with passengers and bundles of newspapers for the nearby towns. Over the airport hovers a helicopter directing traffic from the air. A smudge of smoke on the horizon marks a forest fire where other small planes and helicopters carry out their rescue and surveillance missions.

One of the great ironies is that war, or the threat of war, so often spells technical progress. Never has this been more true than in recent years, for military aviation, since 1945, has undergone the most astonishing transformation in its history, and the end is not yet in sight. Planes, reaching for ever greater speeds and heights, have become manned missiles, largely controlled by electronic devices. The plane and the missile, indeed, complement each other. Both carry the atom bomb offensively and are teamed together in elaborate, electronically-controlled continental defense systems like the U.S.-Canadian Norad. And both are served by the new hybrid "aerospace" industry, backed up by countless busy research laboratories and subsidiary industries. No sooner are new products off the ground than they become obsolete, and still newer ones move from the drawing boards to the factories. The aerospace industry is fed largely by the military, but its mind is on the future.

Priority again goes to the British for the beginning of this revolution. Soon after the war, determined to exploit their new jet engines, they began planning both jet transports and a military air fleet of the most advanced type, with nuclear capability. Unveiled in the early 1950's, their military planes included three huge, four-jet bombers, the Victor, Valiant, and Vulcan, and several swift jet and turboprop fighters, notably the world's first twin-jet, delta-wing fighter, the Javelin. The delta wing, pioneered in

Germany, appeared on the great Vulcan bomber and was soon to be taken up by the Americans.

The brave British lead was not to last. The Americans and the Russians, building spottily since the war, could not yet match the British fleet. The Americans had a series of all-weather fighters, and by 1953 their first supersonic fighter, the F-100 Super Sabre ; also the superb, swept-wing, six-jet B-47 medium bomber, flown as early as 1947. But from 1948 to 1956 they had to rely, for an intercontinental atom bomb carrier, on the hybrid B-36, with mixed jet and piston engines. The Russians had produced their first jet bomber, the Il-28 by 1950 (similar to the British Canberra of the same period), and their fast Mig-17 by 1953 ; but after Korea, as the Cold War grew more intense, both nations began to bring out a coordinated series of jet warplanes, much as the British had done a few years earlier (for every year counted !). The fact that both countries did manage to keep roughly abreast of each other in these years, in quality if not always in quantity, may have had a lot to do with the preservation of the peace.

Like the Americans, the Russians began to build up a force of strategic bombers. The four-jet Bison was introduced in 1953. In 1955 the American B-52 began to replace the B-36 in the Strategic Air Command. The American B-47 was matched by the Russian Badger Tu-16 in 1954. The Mig-19 and 21 appeared in 1955-56 while the Americans were building up their supersonic "century" series—the delta-winged F-102 and F-106, the light F-104 Starfighter, the heavy F-105 Thunderchief. All of these planes were armed variously with heavy cannon and lethal missiles. Both countries put

stress, too, on helicopters, the Russian's jet MI-6 being the largest in the world. Finally, the American B-58, the first delta-wing, supersonic bomber, capable of speeds around 1,400 miles per hour, seems already to have been matched by a heavier, delta-wing Russian bomber glimpsed in 1961. An American specialty is the giant, *Forrestal*-type carrier (the latest is atom-powered), capable of launching both fighters and atom bomb carriers anywhere in the world. A whole series of powerful jet fighters, including the delta-wing Douglas A4D Skyhawk, the F8U Crusader, and the Grumman Tiger, have been developed to fit the needs of these carriers.

In the struggle for mastery since World War II both Russia and the United States have equipped their allies with military planes. The Russian Migs fly everywhere in the Communist bloc. Nato used Sabres for years, many of them built in Canada, but has turned to many different types since then, including the F-104 Starfighter. For the next generation it is heartening to see that British and continental firms are joining American firms to furnish the latest Nato planes, many of them of European origin. As in the civil field, European manufacturers are now producing fine planes. Notable is the French Mirage-III—delta-winged, supersonic and powered by both a rocket and jets—and its heavier, bomber sister, the Mirage-IV, as well as the fighters, Etendard-IV and the Mystère series. Sweden's jets, especially the double-delta, supersonic Draken, rank second to none.

Today's military plane, flying faster than the speed of sound and armed with missiles or the atom bomb, is one of the most potent engines of destruction ever known. Yet if one looks at modern aviation as a whole it is seen to be far too varied, and is moving far too fast, to be tied down to the simple dichotomy of war or peace. The military advances of today often become the peacetime advantages of tomorrow. And to measure a nation's airpower only in terms of destructive power is misleading. Aviation can best be judged, perhaps, in the light of problems solved (whether for war or peace)— by the Montgolfiers, the Wrights, by Count von Zeppelin, Santos-Dumont, Whittle. Today the problems throng more than ever, testifying to the vitality of this young science.

Most of today's problems can be summed up in one word : speed. The pursuit of speed requires new materials to withstand the stresses and heating of supersonic flight ; new forms of power, the ramjet, rocket engine, atomic power, to push planes faster and further ; new aerodynamic designs to master the problems of high velocities at great heights. Most of these have been tested in the X-15 research plane, latest of a line of American rocket-powered test vehicles, including the X-1, which broke the sound barrier before the British did. The X-15 has flown over 59 miles high and over 4,000 miles per hour and has withstood friction temperatures of almost 1,200° F. Next will come the Dynasoar, part missile, part plane, designed to leave the atmosphere and glide home under human control. But this begins to get into a subject which will be examined in a later book in this series, *A History of Rockets and Space.*

Closer to earth the new supersonic, delta-winged jet airliners will, in a few short years,

103 Massed parachutists, dropped from huge military transports, descend in simulated attack. Atomic weapons have rendered obsolete the traditional grappling of huge land armies. In the future troops will fight in small, highly organized, mobile units. Hence airborne troops, which can be rushed to a danger area as soon as required, take on a new importance.

104 *U.S. Air Force B-58
supersonic bomber is one of the
most advanced of military
planes. With its compact
construction, delta wing and
four powerful jets it can fly at
twice the speed of sound. Its
revolutionary design and
performance have already
influenced the planning for the
civil aircraft of the future, in
which supersonic speeds and
delta-wing designs play a
prominent part.*

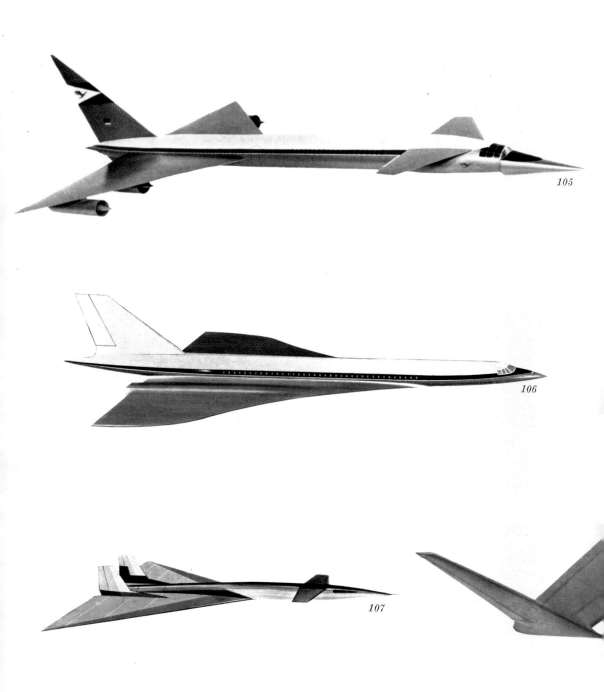

105

106

107

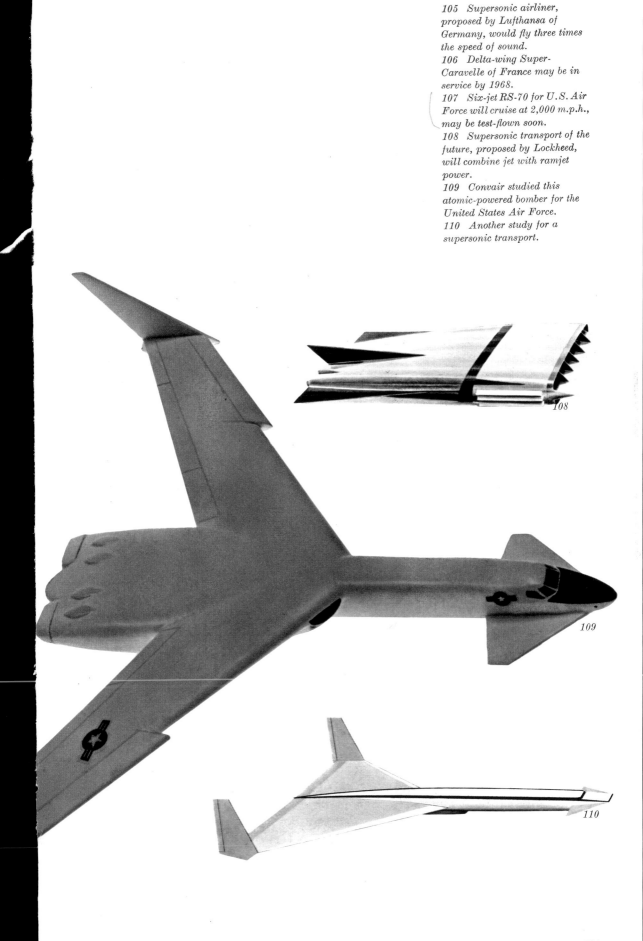

105 *Supersonic airliner, proposed by Lufthansa of Germany, would fly three times the speed of sound.*
106 *Delta-wing Super-Caravelle of France may be in service by 1968.*
107 *Six-jet RS-70 for U.S. Air Force will cruise at 2,000 m.p.h., may be test-flown soon.*
108 *Supersonic transport of the future, proposed by Lockheed, will combine jet with ramjet power.*
109 *Convair studied this atomic-powered bomber for the United States Air Force.*
110 *Another study for a supersonic transport.*

111

be carrying several hundred passengers between New York and Paris in a few hours—at two or three times the speed of sound. A close relative is the forthcoming American RS-70 reconnaissance strike plane, which will cruise at 2,000 miles per hour. Later airliners may be propelled by ramjet engines, taking over from jets at high speed, or may be fueled by atomic power.

These big planes mean bigger problems. Today's jets already need two miles of runway. Air terminals like Orly at Paris or Idlewild at New York are being rushed to completion to accomodate them, but may soon be too small. Ironically, another aspect of aeronautical research today could well render the airport obsolete. Vertical takeoff (VTOL), or short takeoff (STOL) planes of all types, military and civilian, are being actively studied. Helicopters are rapidly widening their scope and usefulness. They range today from large-sized military transports—of increasing importance in the mobile, fast-moving ground warfare of the atomic age—and passenger carriers between airports and cities, to tiny, "do-it-yourself" private rotary planes, many of which are little more than flying armchairs. There is even a flying man (reminiscent of the beginnings of flight !), airborne on invisible jet streams.

The future of aviation may be vast, but it is also quite unpredictable. One constant remains : the enthusiasm and passion of the men and women, today as in the past, who have made it what it is. Jacqueline Cochran, famed aviatrix, has written : "The trouble is that we of the present generation were born too soon. But that will also be said by the next generation, for the flight of man is endless."

111 "... for the flight of man is endless."

chronology

1505 Leonardo da Vinci makes the first detailed analysis of the mechanics of flight.

1670 Jesuit monk Francesco Lana proposes airship raised by evacuated copper globes; deplores idea that such machines might be used in warfare.

1766 English scientist, Henry Cavendish, discovers hydrogen, then called "inflammable air."

1782 Joseph Montgolfier invents the hot-air balloon.

1783 The Montgolfier brothers' balloon makes first public ascension at Annonay, France, on June 4.

1783 The first hydrogen-filled balloon is launched by Jacques Charles and the Robert brothers, Paris, August 27.

1783 A cock, a sheep and a duck are carried aloft in a Montgolfière at Versailles, September 19.

1783 The first man to leave the earth in a balloon, Pilâtre de Rozier, makes test flights in a tethered Montgolfière during October.

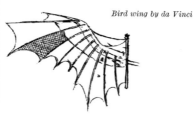

Bird wing by da Vinci

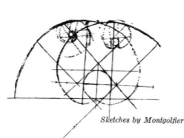

Sketches by Montgolfier

1783 The first men to travel through the air, Pilâtre de Rozier and the Marquis d'Arlandes, ascend from the gardens of La Muette outside Paris on November 21.

1783 Charles and the younger Robert make a 27-mile trip from Paris to Nesle in a hydrogen balloon, December 1.

1785 Jean-Pierre Blanchard and Dr. John Jeffries cross the English Channel in a balloon, January 7.

1785 Pilâtre de Rozier becomes the first aerial casualty as the hybrid hydrogen and hot-air balloon in which he was attempting to cross the English Channel catches fire and burns, June 15.

1794 A captive balloon first used for military observation at siege of Maubeuge, June 2.

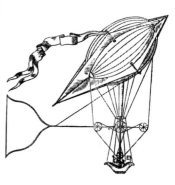

French dirigible, 1814

1797 André-Jacques Garnerin makes first long parachute descent, over Paris, October 22.

1804 Gay-Lussac mounts to 22,892 ft. in a scientific balloon ascension, September 16.

1808 George Cayley of England, called "the father of the airplane," tests his first glider.

1809 George Cayley publishes the first realistic theory of the airplane.

1836 Charles Green, great balloonist of England, makes first long-distance international flight, from London to Nassau in Germany—480 miles in 18 hours.

1842 William S. Henson of England patents his "Aerial Steam Carriage."

1848 John Stringfellow flies a motorized model airplane for 120 ft.

1849 François Arban crosses the Alps for the first time by air

Joseph Montgolfier

Jacques Charles

Blanchard balloon, 1784

Giffard's dirigible

as his balloon travels from Marseilles to Stubini.

52 Henri Giffard makes the first successful motor-driven flight in history, from Paris to Trappes, in his dirigible.

358 First aerial photographs taken by Félix Nadar over Paris.

359 John Wise of the United States makes a balloon flight of over 625 miles, and carries the first airmail, as he flies from St. Louis to Henderson, New York.

862 American Professor T. S. C. Lowe organizes observation balloon service for the Union army during the Civil War.

863 Viscount de Ponton d'Amécourt builds and flies a steam-powered helicopter.

868 England's first Aeronautical Exhibition, at the Crystal Palace in London, features John Stringfellow's model triplane and a lightweight steam engine.

870 During the Prussian siege of Paris a balloon service is set up to keep in touch with the outside world. Altogether 66 balloons left the city,

carrying mail, passengers and carrier pigeons for a return flight.

1872 Alphonse Pénaud's model airplane, the "planophore," exhibited at the Tuileries, flies 180 ft.

1873 John Wise attempts to cross the Atlantic in his giant balloon, crashes 40 miles from New York.

1877 Enrico Forlanini's steam-powered helicopter reaches a height of 41 ft. in free flight.

1883 The electrically-driven dirigible of the Tissandier brothers makes its first flight on October 8.

1884 Renard and Krebs dirigible, "La France," makes first successful round trip flight starting from the Chalais Meudon park.

1890 Clément Ader skims over the ground in his motor-driven "Eole" for 53 yards, October 9.

1891 Otto Lilienthal makes his first flight in a glider.

1896 Samuel Langley's 16-ft., steam-driven model airplane, "Aerodrome No. 5," flies

3,200 ft. over the Potomac River, May 6.

1896 Otto Lilienthal crashes to his death from a biplane glider, after having made some 2,000 glider flights, August 9.

1897 First aerial exploration into the Arctic : Andrée, Strindberg, and Fraenkel leave Spitzbergen for North Pole in a balloon, are lost.

1900 Count von Zeppelin's first rigid dirigible cruises successfully over Lake of Constance, July 3.

1901 Santos-Dumont flies from Saint-Cloud around Eiffel Tower and back in dirigible No. 6 in less than half an hour, winning Henri Deutsch prize, October 19.

1903 French dirigible "Lebaudy" makes first powered cross-country trip, 39 miles from Moisson to Paris, November 2.

1903 Samuel Langley's "Aerodrome" crashes into Potomac, December 8.

1903 Wright brothers make first sustained flight in a motor-driven airplane, at Kitty Hawk, December 17.

Pilâtre de Rozier

Jean-Pierre Blanchard

Cayley's "convertiplane," 1843

Count Zeppelin's pilot licence

Farman's first airplane

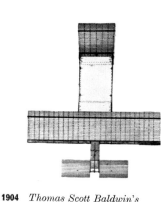

Gnome engine

Aviatrix de la Roche

1904 *Thomas Scott Baldwin's "California Arrow," America's first dirigible, is tested by Roy Knabenshue, August 3.*

1905 *Orville Wright makes first flight of over half an hour at Dayton, October 5.*

1906 *Santos-Dumont makes first public airplane flight in Europe, at Bagatelle, September 13.*

1907 *Paul Cornu makes the first flight in a helicopter, near Lisieux, November 13.*

1908 *First official flight of over one kilometer made by Henri Farman at Issy-les-Moulineaux, January 13.*

1908 *Henri Farman becomes the first airplane passenger, flying with Léon Delagrange at Issy, March 28.*

1908 *The American, Glenn Curtiss, wins "Scientific American" cup with flight of just over a mile, July 4.*

1908 *The U.S. War Department accepts its first military dirigible, built by Thomas Scott Baldwin and powered by a Glenn Curtiss motor, August.*

1908 *Wilbur Wright flies in France ending the three-year moratorium on flying by the Wrights, and astounding the French, August.*

1908 *The airplane's first victim, Lt. Selfridge, is killed in the crash of a plane piloted by Orville Wright, who was demonstrating it before the Army, September 17.*

1908 *Henri Farman makes the first cross-country flight in an airplane, flying from Bouy to Rheims in 20 minutes, October 30.*

1909 *Louis Blériot flies the English Channel, from Calais to Dover, July 25.*

1909 *A Wright Flyer accepted by United States Army as world's first military plane, August 2.*

1909 *World's first major air meet, at Rheims, August 22-29.*

1910 *First air meet held in the United States at Los Angeles, January 10 to 20.*

1910 *First hydroplane flown at Martiques, France, by Henri Fabre, March 28.*

1910 *First flight across the Lake of Geneva by Armand Dufaux in a plane built by himself and his brother, Henri, August 28.*

1910 *Géo Chavez flies over Alps from Brig to Domodossola, is killed on landing, September 23.*

1910 *The dirigible "Clement-Bayard II" makes first crossing of the Channel, France to England, October 16.*

1910 *The German Delag line begins world's first scheduled passenger service with the Zeppelin, "Deutschland."*

1911 *Eugene Ely, Curtiss pilot, makes landing on deck of U.S.S. "Pennsylvania," takes off again, January 18.*

1911 *First non-stop airplane flight from London to Paris, by Pierre Prier, April 12.*

1911 *U.S. Navy accepts first seaplane, a Curtiss hydro-plane, in July.*

1911 *First use of the airplane in war during Italo-Turkish War.*

1911 *Calbraith P. Rodgers makes the first coast-to-coast flight in the United States, from New York to California, September 17 to December 10.*

1913 *World's first four-engined plane, "Le Grand," designed by Igor Sikorsky of Russia, flown on May 13.*

1913 *Roland Garros crosses the Mediterranean from Saint-Raphaël to Bizerte, September 23.*

1913 *Maurice Prévost flies his Deperdussin monoplane at a*

Dijon meet, 1910

Zeppelin ZR-3, 1924

Poster, 1930's

Santos-Dumont

record speed of over 200 km.
an hour, September 29.

1914 The first year of World War I
sees the start of combat
between airplanes.

1915 The first tentative strategic
bombing missions carried out
by the British and French
during the spring.

1917 First giant German bombers
appear over London,
replacing the Zeppelins.

1918 First mass air campaign in
history carried out during
St. Mihiel offensive in
September, with nearly
1,500 Allied planes under
command of General William
E. Mitchell.

1918 Official United States airmail
service begins with first link
between Washington and
New York, May 15.

1919 Germany's Luftreederei opens
first postwar scheduled
airline, Berlin-Leipzig-
Weimar, February 5.

1919 Société Farman flies
passengers from Paris to
London in a converted
bomber, the beginning of
international air travel,
February 8.

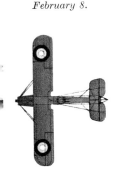

U.S. DH-4

1919 First crossing of the Atlantic
by air as U.S. Navy flying
boat, NC-4, flies from
Newfoundland to the Azores,
May 16-17.

1919 First airplane to cross the
Atlantic : British officers,
Alcock and Whitten-Brown
fly from Newfoundland to
Ireland in a Vickers-Vimy
bomber, June 14-15.

1919 First round-trip crossing of
the Atlantic by British
dirigible, R-34, July 2-13.

1919 Captain Ross Smith flies a
Vickers-Vimy bomber from
England to Australia,
November 12-December 10.

1920 Italian aviators Ferrarin and
Masiero fly from Rome to
Tokyo, February 11-May 31.

1920 First flight across the
Sahara, by Vuillemin and
Chalus, February 18.

1921 First coast-to-coast, day and
night government airmail
flights inaugurated in the
United States in February.

1922 First crossing of the South
Atlantic by hydroplane, from
Lisbon to Rio de Janeiro by
Sacadura Cabral and Gago
Coutinho, March 30-June 5.

1923 La Cierva's autogiro makes its
first successful flight at
Madrid, Spain, January 31.

1923 France forms the national
airline, Air Union (became
Air France ten years later).
The Belgian Sabena is also
formed.

1923 First non-stop flight from
New York to San Francisco
by Lts. Macready and Kelly,
May 2-3.

1923 First refueling in flight by
Lts. Smith and Richter, at
San Diego, California,
June 26.

1924 Four Air Service "World
Cruisers" set off around the
world on April 6. Two make
it in 15 days flying time.

1924 Imperial Airways formed in
England.

1925 German airlines consolidated
into Lufthansa.

1926 Lt. Comdr. Richard E. Byrd
of U.S. Navy and Floyd
Bennett make the first flight
over the North Pole, May 2.

1926 First complete crossing of the
polar ice cap by the airship
"Norge," carrying Amundsen,
Nobile, and Ellsworth from
Spitzbergen across the North
Pole to Alaska, May 11-14.

1927 Charles Lindbergh makes
first non-stop solo flight
from New York to Paris,
May 20-21.

1927 Clarence Chamberlin and
Charles Levine fly non-stop
from New York to Berlin,
June 4.

1927 Lts. Lester Maitland and
Albert Hegenberger fly from
Oakland, California, to
Hawaii, June 28.

1927 Commander Byrd flies Fokker
trimotor, "America," across
Atlantic, crash-landing off
Normandy, July 1.

1927 Sir Alan Cobham flies
20,000 miles around Africa
in a seaplane.

1928 The "Southern Cross"
trimotor, commanded by the
Australian, Charles
Kingsford-Smith, flies from

English Spitfires

Churchill at war

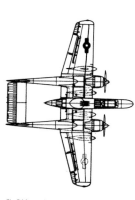

California to Australia,
May 31 to June 9.

1929 Dirigible "Graf Zeppelin,"
under command of Hugo
Eckener, flies around the
world, August 8-29.

1929 Commander Byrd flies over
the South Pole in a Ford
trimotor, November 28.

1930 U.S. airlines formed—
American Airways,
January 25, and United Air
Lines, June 30.

1930 First non-stop flight from Paris
to New York by Dieudonné
Costes and Maurice Bellonte
of France, September 1-2.

1930 Frank Whittle in England
takes out first patents on his
jet engine.

1931 T.W.A. (Trans World
Airlines) organized in the
United States, February 13.

1931 Professor Auguste Piccard
makes first stratospheric
balloon flight, 51,775 ft., on
May 26.

1931 Wiley Post and Harold Gatty
make record-breaking flight
around the world (8 days,
15 hours, and 51 minutes) in
their Lockheed monoplane,
"Winnie Mae," June.

1931 Dirigible "Graf Zeppelin"
inaugurates first commercial
transatlantic passenger
service, between Germany
and Brazil, August 29.

1932 Amelia Earhart (first woman
passenger to fly the Atlantic)
becomes first woman to fly
it alone, May 20-21.

1933 Wiley Post makes solo flight
around the world in the
"Winnie Mae," covering
15,596 miles in $7\frac{1}{4}$ days. July.

1935 Hans von Ohain takes out
first German patents on a jet
engine.

1936 Dirigible "Hindenburg"
makes first scheduled
commercial flight across North
Atlantic, from Frankfurt to
Lakehurst, New Jersey, May 6.

1936 The United States Air Corps
accepts the first two B-17 Flying Fortress strategic bombers.

1937 The "Hindenburg" burns at
Lakehurst, May 6.

1937 Three Russians make the
first non-stop flight from
Russia to the United States
via the polar route, flying
from Moscow to Portland,
Oregon, June 18-20.

1939 Flight of the world's first
turbojet aircraft, the German
He-178, on August 27.

1939 World War II opens with
German attack on Poland,
September 1.

1940 German aerial "blitzkrieg"
attack on France and the
Lowlands, followed by
Battle of Britain, in which
airpower averts invasion.

1941 England's first jet aircraft,
the Gloster E28/39, powered
by a Whittle engine, makes its
first flight, May 15.

1941 First extensive airborne attack,
by Germany on British-held
Crete, May 20.

1941 Japanese attack on U.S.
Pacific bases at Pearl Harbor

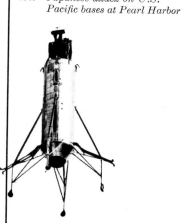

and in Philippines,
December 7—a classic use of
airpower.

1942 The first American jet, the
Bell XP-59A, makes its first
flight on October 1.

1944 The first operational jets, the
German Me-262's, enter
combat.

1944 German V-1 flying bombs and
V-2 rockets bombard London.

1945 First atom bomb, on
Hiroshima, helps bring the
war to an end, August 6.

1947 The Bell X-1 research rocket
plane breaks through the
sonic barrier, October 14.

1948 The British DH-108, the first
jet plane to break the sound
barrier, September 16.

1950 The Korean War breaks out—
first jet combat between
Russian-built Mig-15's and
American Sabre F-86's.

1952 The British De Havilland
Comet, world's first jet
transport, enters service.

1954 A Scandinavian DC-6 makes
first "great circle" flight over
Arctic from Los Angeles to
Copenhagen, via Greenland.

1958 Pan American launches first
American commercial jet
service between New York
and Europe, October 26.

1961 A U.S. Air Force supersonic
B-58 bomber flies from
New York to Paris in 3 hours,
19 minutes, May 26.

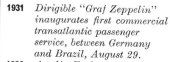

*Among those who have assisted
in the preparation of this book
grateful acknowledgment must be
made to the following members
of the ENI staff:
Helen Muller, Eric Tschumi,
Nicolas Bouvier, as well as to
Charles Dollfus and the Musée
de l'air, both of Paris,
to Interavia Magazine, Geneva, and
Aviation Week Magazine, Geneva.*

credits

Printed in Switzerland